OF
PRIMEVAL STEPS
AND
FUTURE LEAPS

OF
PRIMEVAL STEPS
AND
FUTURE LEAPS

An Essay on the
Emergence of Human Beings,
the Source of Women's Oppression,
and the Road to Emancipation

by
Ardea Skybreak

BANNER PRESS
CHICAGO

Banner Press, Chicago

Cover photograph by John Reader
Courtesy Mary D. Leakey

Library of Congress Cataloging in Publication Data

Skybreak, Ardea.
    Of primeval steps and future leaps.

    Bibliography: p.
    1. Human evolution.   2. Women—Evolution.   3. Social
evolution.   I. Title.
GN281.S56   1984   573.2   84-24448

ISBN 0-916650-19-7

OF
PRIMEVAL STEPS
AND
FUTURE LEAPS

In hunter-gatherer societies, men hunt and women stay at home. This strong bias persists in most agricultural and industrial societies and, on that basis alone, appears to have a genetic origin. . . . My own guess is that the genetic bias is intense enough to cause a substantial division of labor in even the most free and most egalitarian of future societies. . . . Even with identical education and equal access to all professions, men are likely to continue to play a disproportionate role in political life, business and science.

E.O. Wilson

The expectations of theory color perception to such a degree that new notions seldom arise from facts collected under the influence of old pictures of the world. New pictures must cast their influence before facts can be seen in different perspective.

Niles Eldredge and S.J. Gould

Neither the emergence of the human species nor the development of human society to the present was predetermined or followed predetermined pathways. There is no transcendent will or agent which has conceived and shaped all such development, and nature and history should not be treated as such—as Nature and History. Rather, such development occurs through the dialectical interplay between necessity and accident and in the case of human history between underlying material forces and the conscious activity and struggle of people.

Bob Avakian

Introduction

We call ourselves human beings, *Homo sapiens*, and we inhabit the planet earth. But where did we come from? What were we like in the beginning of our species' life? Were we bloodthirsty brutes? Were the females of our species helpless creatures dependent on Mighty Males for their very survival? How did we live?

We are, as humans, very particular in that we have always posed such questions and sought to know all about the universe and ourselves within it, from our earliest origins to the future before us. Times marked by intensifying social contradictions have always tended to fuel raging debates over a wide assortment of fundamental questions, partly because the straining of the social fabric calls into question the validity of all previously established thought and institutions, and partly because the answers to these questions seem to matter so much more.

Today, as we are literally having to confront the possibility of our own self-imposed annihilation, there are those who would shy away from broad-ranging questions of any sort and purposefully narrow their sights, pleading that they can only deal with one atomized bit of motion at a time and retreating into various brands of agnosticism and general know-nothingism. Others, however, question things as never before and plunge into the fray as many long-held scientific and philosophical notions are being dislodged and tossed into the air: How does matter really move? Will the known universe continually expand, will it eventually contract, or is it alternately doing both? Was there one Big Bang or many, separated by periods of relative "rest"? Was this in fact part of an even larger process? Do new things originate only through a gradual accumulation of change, or are there sudden discontinuities and leaps in material processes? Is change ever ascending towards greater complexity, towards some higher realm of Perfection, or are there twists and turns and innumerable potential pathways in all material processes, some of which lead to dead ends while others generate newness?

Debates currently raging over such questions do not represent simply idle intellectual pursuits, but matters of vital importance. Where new understanding rises to challenge the old, conventional wisdom often refuses to yield the stage. This does not merely express stubborn ignorance or limited understanding but reflects certain class relations which buttress those theories and certain class interests which dictate that, despite evident falsehood, the old be preserved and canonized insofar as it serves a useful ideological and political function in the existing social order.

Nowhere is this more true than in the debate over the origins and early evolution of human beings and human social behavior. The following essay was initially conceived as a vehicle for a critical examination and evaluation of some "new models" concerning the origin of our species which have appeared in recent years. More specifically, it seemed that at long last attempts were being made to seriously challenge and refute a number of scientifically unsubstantiated origin myths which had become well entrenched in the popular consciousness and which promoted biodeterministic views of so-called human nature. It is no accident that the social turmoil and upheavals which posed serious challenges to the established order of things in so many spheres of social relations and in so many parts of the world during the late '60s and '70s would have provided impetus for many to question such assumptions. Because the traditional and broadly popularized origin myths all seem characterized by a high degree of male chauvinism and androcentrism, the task of reexamining our origins and early evolution has been of particular interest to feminists and others concerned with combating the oppression of women in modern society.

A good part of this work will therefore be devoted to an examination and critical appraisal of two attempts at origin-myth refutation, *The Descent of Woman* by Elaine Morgan and *On Becoming Human* by Nancy Makepeace Tanner. Both books have found wide and even somewhat overlapping audiences. If Morgan's book has won little respect in scientific circles, it is nonetheless quite popular—and its lack of scientific "respectability" hardly means that it could not serve to uncover truth, nor still less that it should not be taken seriously. In a certain sense, Tanner and Morgan concentrate two different and almost polar-opposite methods of refuting the various myths and distortions which have permeated reconstructions of our origins for decades: one seeks to refute the myths through wielding scientific materialism, the other responds with what is essentially a countermyth.

The discussion of one of these attempts will show it to be a teacher by negative example and provide some insights into the potential pitfalls that arise when attempting to refute faulty assumptions and theoretical constructs with faulty methodology. In this case the particular methodological errors have been raised to the level of caricature, but they are nevertheless quite prevalent in somewhat more subtle form in much of the more serious scientific literature in evolutionary biology, where they serve not only to promote "bad science," but also, in some cases, to buttress reactionary ideological and political views. It is hoped that this essay will contribute to the ongoing polemic on some of these questions.

A critical examination of the second attempt at origin-myth refutation reveals it to be one of the best examples to date of a serious reexamination of our origins as a species. It is fresh, provocative, and an important contribution to understanding the process of our emergence in its own right. Moreover, it provides much food for thought for anyone seeking to determine what (if any) connections exist between our origins as a species and a variety of problems of modern social relations and organization. In particular, while its scope is limited to a reconstruction of the period of our earliest divergence from the apes, its analyses and conclusions are valuable stepping stones for exploring the origins and ongoing bases for the subjugation of females and their domination by males in the most varied of modern human societies.

This essay is a case in point. In the course of evaluating the data and analyses on which Tanner's model is founded, it became apparent that one could go further and begin to fill some gaps in our understanding of what must have been the earliest basis for social inequalities between men and women. The latter part of this essay will seek to explore this area, drawing from some of the greatly expanded body of modern anthropological data on foraging societies as well as from tentative reconstructions of our earliest origins. As part of this, it will attempt a beginning reassessment of the pioneering and overall extremely insightful contribution to an understanding of the causes of the subjugation of women which can be found in Engels's *The Origin of the Family, Private Property, and the State.*

Social science took a gigantic historical leap in the mid- to late 19th century with the introduction of the Marxist method of dialectical and historical material- ism, which served not only to probe the material under- pinnings of various social systems at various points in history (in contrast to so many religious and other idealist interpretations) but which also and for the first time provided a theoretical framework through which it became possible to examine social structures in their motion and development, rather than as frozen slices of time. In contrast to previous static and compartmen- talized views of history, it now became possible to discern and analyze factors mediating breaks and leaps in human social relations and organization. This con- tinually developing science has, since the time of Marx, contributed a great deal to our understanding of a wide variety of social systems marked by class structures (in- cluding essentially slave, feudal, capitalist, and socialist systems) and continues to provide provocative insights into future means of social organization, including the prospect for the complete elimination of class divisions on a global scale.

The period which pre-dates the emergence of classes has remained more elusive. Yet, as Marx was quick to point out, classes are a relatively recent phenomenon. They came into being at specific points in history and in relation to discernible material developments. While human social systems devoid of classes have persisted into this century, they have so long been the rare excep- tion rather than the rule that it is often difficult for us to conceive of a time when the converse was true. Yet we know that millions of years elapsed since our ancestors first diverged from the apes, and that our species as such goes back at least 100,000 years, during which time it has spread across the planet, originating varied means of subsistence and of cultural expression—although classes have only existed for a few thousand of those years.

Engels, in close collaboration with Marx, initiated a beginning exploration of the material factors which had mediated the transition of pre-class societies to class-based systems, drawing as much as he could from the early body of anthropological data, including that which contrasted with orthodox views of the day. In so doing, Engels was able (as we shall see) to gain some valuable insights into a number of aspects of human social organization through history, including on the question of the material basis for the subjugation of women throughout history. There is still much which can be learned from these insights. On the other hand, the sciences of anthropology, paleontology, and evolutionary biology were in their infancy in Engels's day and much raw material has accumulated since that time which must be studied and analyzed anew. Furthermore, the cornerstone scientific method given us by Marx and Engels has itself undergone significant development since their time and is continually being further developed. Those who would dismiss the early contributions with a wave of the hand are poor scientists who are closing themselves off to a wealth of historical and methodological insights. But those who are content to rest with the understanding of the past and who never seek to push it further are ossified in their thinking and have little grasp of the Marxist method.

What factors were originally responsible for the earliest forms of social inequalities between the sexes? At what point did they come into play? Do they pre-date classes, or was pre-class society characterized by perfect harmony between the sexes? And what (if anything) can the answers to such questions tell us about the factors which ensure the ongoing suppression and subjugation of women in the modern world? If what is explored and argued in this essay serves to spark further debate and investigation of these crucial questions among a variety of people, both men and women, of varied perspectives, I will deem it to have been successful.

I

People over the centuries have creatively concocted a dazzling array of idealist fairy tales about human origins. These have almost always boiled down to crediting some invisible hand, some higher being or force, some god or gods, with the creation of Man (and of Woman, as an afterthought). Such theories have of course never been based on any material evidence and are untestable in principle and by their very design. Yet they served to quell nagging questions, and continue to be of particular value to the efforts of successive ruling classes to explain and justify their favored systems and to discourage any questioning of the "natural order of things" which is said to correspond to some "divine plan." Of course, religious myths in general, and divine-creation myths in particular, have never succeeded absolutely in preventing rebellions of the oppressed and the overthrow of archaic social orders in the course of human history, but they have always served as a useful brake on such processes and they have proven very resilient.

While religious origin myths cannot be expected to

die out completely as long as there remains a material basis for oppression in the world, there is no denying that they were dealt a collective body blow in the late 19th century. At a time of a general flowering of materialist analyses which accompanied the rise of the bourgeoisie and the developing contradiction between it and the proletarians it exploited and oppressed, Darwin's theory of evolution by natural selection burst onto the scene, providing for the first time an understanding of the basic and most important mechanisms for the origin and evolution of the great variety of plant and animal species on earth—including *Homo sapiens*! This notion that we were not created "in god's image," but were animals evolved from lowly apes, of course stirred up great controversy and resistance. But there was no escaping the fact that a mechanism for evolutionary change had been proposed which could be tested and verified, and which in fact has since been validated experimentally. Today the process of natural selection is an undeniable fact, and in the mere 100 or so years since Darwin we have raised to a qualitatively higher level our understanding of the origins, development, and change of living organisms, and opened the door to a scientific exploration of our own origins.

But in the post-Darwinian era many new "origin myths" have been generated: various breeds of "Social-Darwinists" greatly vulgarized and distorted Darwin's theories and then transposed them to the realm of human social relations, content to replace the hand of god with the legacy of the apes. Ruthless economic competition, territorial expansion, and the oppression and subjugation of entire peoples were all justified as simple and unavoidable continuations in the sociocultural realm of the so-called "survival of the fittest." While such crude Social-Darwinism later came to be recognized as yet another pseudoscientific fraud with no basis in biological evolution, it has since been replaced by

somewhat more sophisticated and updated biodeterminist origin myths which still explain current "problems"
in human social relations (such as sexual inequalities,
national oppression, wars, etc.) as consequences of our
earliest evolutionary origins. The underlying implication is always that it's not much use trying to change
some of these things because unfortunately we were
made that way, we have certain "biological impera-
tives," etc. In recent decades such views were fueled and
popularized by writers such as Konrad Lorenz, one of the
pioneers of ethology (the study of animal behavior), and
such vulgar pop anthropologists as Lionel Tiger, Desmond Morris, and Robert Ardrey. Since the mid-1970s
the school of biodeterminism has been once again updated and given a significant shot in the arm with the
development and promotion of sociobiology which,
when extended to humans, further purports to explain
social behavior in terms of the supposed results of
natural selection for or against certain behaviors. As will
be shown and stressed in the course of this book, the
Achilles' heel of this reactionary school of thought is
that it consistently takes as its starting point a notion for
which there is no evidence, which is biologically extremely unlikely, and which, as a general explanation of
human social behavior and as a basis for theories of
"human nature," is completely erroneous: the assumption that complex human social behaviors can be tied to
specific genetic programs.[1]

---

[1]Two excellent critiques of an assortment of such biodeterminist
views can be found in Gould 1981 and Chorover 1980. As this book
was being prepared for publication, I obtained a copy of the newly
published book *Not in Our Genes* by R.C. Lewontin, Steven Rose,
and Leon J. Kamin. A quick first reading reveals it to be a very
welcome addition to the critique of biodeterministic theories of
individual human behaviors and human social organization. In
addition to vivid exposures of the unfounded biological assumptions and faulty methodology underlying so much of what passes

How in fact did humans develop? Popular reconstructions of the last few decades most often run something like this: Our ancestors were primarily forest-
dwelling apes in the area which is now Eastern Africa.
They moved through the trees and were primarily vege-
tarian. So far so good. Then, the story goes, some of these
apes left the trees and moved onto the open savannas,
finding them rich in big game. Then, "with strong
pressure on them to increase their prey-killing prowess,
they became more upright—fast, better runners" (Desmond Morris, cited in Morgan 1971, p. 6). In becoming
the Mighty Hunter, Man lost his coat of fur to prevent
overheating in the course of the hunt and immediately
invented weapons: "In the first evolutionary hour of the
human emergence," says Robert Ardrey (cited in Morgan 1971, p. 8), "we became sufficiently skilled in the
use of weapons to render redundant our natural primate
daggers"—that is to say, our teeth. Thus, according to
this view, weapons were the key element in separating
Man from beast.

And "Man" here does mean the male of the species,
the only sex thought to have played much of a role in the
divergence from the apes. The Mighty Hunters traipsing
all over the savannas killing big game with their brand
new weapons were thus supposedly able to provide food
and protection for the females and young, who were
presumably sitting helpless in the background. Man
evolved speech, in this scheme of things, to better coordinate his hunting activities, and went on to develop art,
ritual, etc., for the same purpose. He formed bigger

---

as legitimate theory in the realm of IQ, mental health, male-
female differences, and sociobiological interpretations of social
organization, there is here a refreshing attempt to directly draw out
the reactionary political implications of these theories and to
probe more thoroughly their philosophical and methodological
underpinnings.

social groupings and invented monogamy as a device to insure the "little woman" would be there when he got back from the hunt. And while Tarzan chased about on the hunt, Jane was good enough to evolve bigger buttocks, breasts, lips, etc., and to make herself sexually available at all times in order to please Tarzan and ensure his continuing presence and protection in a hostile environment. Tarzan, meanwhile, formed tight fraternal associations with other males—the better to hunt and to repel predators—and reinforced male group cohesion by being aggressive and territorial towards any outsiders. And so it goes.

Anyone who thinks the above is too much of a caricature of these classical reconstructions should check out some of the popular literature à la Desmond Morris's *Naked Ape*, which, while it may elicit snickers and guffaws in scientific circles today, continues to have broad popular influence. As for the more "serious literature," though more carefully worded, it still promotes many of these same unfounded assumptions concerning the key elements in the transition from ape to human: the emphasis on hunting, men on center stage as the sole innovators, women and young seen as passive or quasi-nonexistent, a high level of aggression, etc. These stories are all loaded with political implications, providing choice material for the claim that women are naturally less competent and men are naturally more aggressive. The overall effect is to create the impression that the subordinate position of women relative to men has been with us from the very beginning and forms part of the natural, if perhaps regrettable, order of things. The idea is also conveyed that human aggression and war are part of the natural packaging, our innate animal side which, do what you will, keeps reasserting itself as part of Mother Nature's program.

By focusing almost exclusively on men, and thus systematically ignoring the role played by half the species, prior reconstructions have been unable to give us much of a real sense of what the transitional populations which diverged from the apes and subsequent hominids were really like, despite much valuable information available from the fossil record and other areas. Social bias has literally blinded researchers to much evidence which was right under their noses.

As is clear from her book *The Descent of Woman*, Elaine Morgan, for one, is justifiably incensed at the grotesque androcentrism of most reconstructions, and sets out to demolish what she calls the Tarzanist model of early human evolution. She picks up, correctly, on how implausible it is that the transitional populations which diverged from the apes could have been made up of passive females and Mighty Hunter males. Such a role division would have necessitated an almost instantaneous switch from small, mainly quadrupedal, fruit- and leaf-eating, tree-dwelling apes, into a hominid form capable of living in the open and able to run at great speeds with newly erect posture, throwing stones with sufficient force and accuracy to kill big animals on a regular basis, and able to digest large amounts of meat. This reconstruction *is*, in fact, ridiculous, and there is good reason to suggest a completely different sequence of events. Such a sequence could be based on evidence from the fossil record (which reveals changes in skeletal structure, diet, tool use, brain expansion, etc.); reconstruction of the types of environments available at the time of the divergence from the apes; comparative studies of our closest living primate relatives; and reviews of the customs and social structures of present-day peoples living in marginal environments with subsistence economies.

But Morgan does not dig into the available information. She simply attempts to replace the old Tarzanist models with yet another imaginative reconstruction which is just as unlikely and unsubstantiated, even if females do come off looking a bit more innovative. She starts off by recalling that the Miocene period, in which our most distant, forest-dwelling ancestors lived, gave way rather abruptly to a period of severe climatic changes. This period, it is thought, saw the extensive rain forest cover of East Africa break up and shrink considerably, while dry, open savannas became more extensive. Morgan postulates that some populations of the ancestral apes were driven into the open, and that, while many probably died off, some individuals must have exhibited a behavioral capacity to adapt to these new environmental conditions and were thereby able to survive, reproduce, and then pass on this new adaptive capacity. The new populations would thus have increasingly diverged from the apes and constituted the first groups of transitional hominids or "pre-people." Thinking that the savannas were altogether too hot and dangerous for these creatures, Morgan further postulates that the key behavioral innovation which signalled the divergence occurred when the females (especially vulnerable because of small canine teeth and burdensome young) escaped from the predators of the open savannas by running into bodies of water (seas and lakes). Others followed and were able to survive and reproduce by occupying waters which were relatively safe from predators and a rich source of food to boot.

This supposed "aquatic phase" in the transition from ape to human was apparently first proposed by Alistair Hardy in 1960 but never pursued. Morgan enthusiastically runs with it, explaining that soon females would have initiated tool use by using pebbles to crack open shellfish which they would then share with their young, and that the whole species would gradually evolve to adapt to a fully aquatic lifestyle. Just to be clear, Morgan is not simply suggesting that early hominids started to exploit the resources of shallows and shore line (which is likely, and suggested by the fact that many fossils in the E. African rift system have been found next to lakes and river beds). No, Morgan is suggesting that these transitional forms started to evolve into a *fully aquatic species* complete with specialized adaptations similar to those of marine mammals. She further postulates that after millions of years of evolution in this direction, they did an about face and reemerged when the droughts ended (at the beginning of the Pleistocene) to resume a terrestrial lifestyle, by this time having become a fully erect, tool-using creature with the rudiments of speech, able to range over a variety of habitats. And the rest is history!

Is this yarn theoretically impossible? Well, not necessarily: there are known cases of terrestrial mammals which have returned to the seas from which all life on earth presumably emerged (the ancestors of whales, dolphins, and sea cows were once terrestrial, for instance). If one is to seriously evaluate and critique Morgan's proposal it is important to have some sense of the actual workings of natural selection and of the process of speciation whereby a new species emerges from an ancestral stock.

For one thing, selection does not operate in any preordained direction. In any given species of plant or animal, different populations exhibit a range of genetic variation, and it is this genetic variation which is the raw material for the evolution of a species by means of natural selection. The selection process itself is "blind"—an individual as a whole is the target of natural selection (as opposed to one or more genes)—and in fact the genes remain "invisible" to selection. This is because what gets selected for or against is a whole organism's *phenotype*, i.e., the external morphological, physiological, and behavioral *manifestation* of its genetic makeup, in its particular interaction with the outside environment. A given *genotype* (genetic makeup) may *exhibit a number of different phenotypic manifestations*, depending on variations in the external environment with which it interacts (including other species).

It has been well documented experimentally that individual organisms with identical genetic makeups can exhibit very different phenotypic manifestations of the same genotype under varying environmental conditions: for instance, a series of genetically identical bean plants obtained through self-fertilization will nonetheless produce beans of very different size in relation to varying ambient conditions (available light, water, nutrients, etc.). Conversely, a similar phenotypic appearance does not necessarily reflect an identical genetic substrate due to the possible "masking" of certain features of the genotype. This is the case, for instance, when individuals carry and transmit the genes for certain inheritable diseases without themselves exhibiting the disease. In all cases, it is the phenotypic manifestation of an organism that is subject to natural selection, which remains "blind" to the underlying genetic makeup.

In passing, I should make clear that I am not suggesting that all evolutionary change takes place at the level of organisms. I am in basic agreement with the orientation expressed by Stephen Jay Gould, for instance, who writes that while "selection can only work on discrete individuals with inherited continuity from ancestor to descendant," different types of individuals (e.g., genes or species), corresponding to different levels of organization of matter, may be subject to selection processes analogous, though not identical, to natural selection operating at the level of individual organisms, in an "analog of what we would call 'differential birth' in natural selection among bodies" (cf. Gould 1983, pp. 166-176). While a further exploration of this particular point is beyond the scope of this essay, it is important to understand that evolutionary biology has long been plagued by problems stemming from a failure to correctly distinguish between different levels of organization of matter and their characteristic features and processes. This is particularly evident today in sociobiology's constant confusion of "properties of sets with properties of members of sets," as Lewontin put it in his 1979 paper. An important step in cutting through this confusion is to correctly understand how natural selection actually does operate at the level of individual organisms.

All natural selection means is that if a particular phenotype's interaction with its environment is such that it produces offspring that are more viable in that environment than other phenotypes, its particular assortment of underlying genes will increase in the population. This in turn can lead to shifts in the population, tending to generalize whatever aspects had conferred the reproductive "edge." Thus it can be said quite simply that "the measure of natural selection is reproductive success" (Dobzhansky, cited in Tanner 1981, p. 161)—no more, no less. Natural selection is an ongoing process in all living things, has been demonstrated experimentally, and is certainly the main, though not the only, mechanism of biological evolutionary change on this planet. It does frequently lead to the emergence of new and specific adaptations in species of plants and animals; however (and this is crucial to understand), natural selection does not operate on the basis of whether something is going to be overall adaptive for a given species.[2]

---

[2]The term "adaptation" is generally ascribed to particular morphological or behavioral features of organisms which seem to enhance their probability of survival and successful reproduction in a given environmental context, and which are postulated (or can be shown) to have evolved in relation to specific environmental features as a result of natural selection at some time in the past. The cryptic coloration and markings of many species which allow individuals to "blend" into their background environment and escape detection by predators is a classical example of such an

Through natural selection the characteristics of individuals leaving more viable offspring tend to increase within a population, regardless of whether this increased reproduction is advantageous to the population as a whole under prevailing circumstances, and regardless of whether associated features may prove disastrous in the long run to the survival of the species. Again, the process of natural selection is blind, not unidirectional or directional in any way, and it is not a process specifically geared *for* adaptation, at any level.

A new species often arises when an isolated, usually small population undergoes a genetic "shift" while reproductively isolated in some fashion from the ancestral stock and then *diverges* to such an extent that it is no longer able to successfully interbreed with the rest of the

---

adaptation. "Organisms are doomed to extinction unless they change continuously in order to keep step with the constantly changing physical and biotic environment. Such changes are ubiquitous since climates change, competitors invade the area, predators become extinct, food sources fluctuate; indeed hardly any component of the environment remains constant" (Mayr 1982, p. 484). There is no doubt that adaptations to features of the environment are common in nature, but the term adaptation has been much abused and applied to many different phenomena. The term is used both to describe an ongoing dialectical process (i.e., the constant interplay between changing organisms and their changing environments), as well as points of relative identity (i.e., the specific features themselves which are the result of natural selection generalizing and "fixing" traits of organisms which contribute to their ability to survive and reproduce). It has recently been suggested that it would be best to restrict the use of the term "adaptation" to those features whose origins can be ascribed to the direct action of natural selection at some point in the past for the function that this feature now performs. This definition would specifically not encompass those features of organisms which may *presently* confer a reproductive advantage, but which may or may not be the product of past natural selection. (For some insights into the complexities and controversies involved in defining adaptation and their biological and social implications, cf. Gould and Lewontin 1979; Gould and Vrba 1982.)

species. It has by definition become a new species. While change never ceases completely and the new species continues to evolve, it may retain its new relative identity for long periods of time; or it may, on the other hand, fairly rapidly go on to further qualitative leaps ranging from extinction to further speciations. Understanding the process of natural selection and speciation is extremely important because many models in evolutionary biology—including many of those which deal with the origin and evolution of the human species—cloak themselves in the Darwinian mantle but base their theories on a number of false assumptions which they treat as facts, though there may be either no evidence to back them up, or even contrary evidence. In fact, such false assumptions are at the heart of the debate raging in evolutionary biology today, and form the underpinning for the whole reactionary pseudoscience of sociobiology, whose repertoire of elaborate myths about the biological determinants of human social behavior Stephen Jay Gould has aptly described as a bunch of "unsupported speculations with political clout" (Gould 1978, p. 532).

Elaine Morgan's book is unfortunately not based on a correct scientific understanding of such processes as adaptation, selection, and speciation, and, as we shall see, reads like a crude compendium of some of the worst methodological errors of both the classical ethologists of the Lorenzian era and the more recent sociobiologists.[3]

---

[3]Konrad Lorenz made many contributions to the science of ethology. He was one of the first to demonstrate that certain simple behavior patterns in some animal species are the product of an interaction between an inheritable genetic program and specific external stimuli required to activate that program. Imprinting in birds is a classical Lorenzian example of such an interaction: newly hatched goslings are genetically programmed to key into the first shape they see after hatching (which is normally the mother goose), and they follow this shape everywhere it goes; but when Lorenz himself was the first shape seen by some hatchlings, they

Returning to Morgan's model, we find that she is determined to convince us that our early evolution passed through a stage of adaptation to aquatic life, and that we then reemerged as a terrestrial mammal. She is not overly bothered by the fact that no other land mammal seems to have accomplished this remarkable back-and-forth trip (her suggestion that elephants may have done the same thing is not convincing; the origins of features she thinks were once "aquatic adaptations," such as the great bulk, hairlessness, the ability to swim using the trunk as a "snorkel," and the shovel-tusks of some elephant ancestors, need not be the characteristics of an aquatic animal—and some, such as the shovel-tusks of some fossils, suggest an inhabitant of swamps

---

became "imprinted" with his image and thereafter followed him around wherever he went! Such interdependence between an apparent genetic blueprint common to the species and external environmental cues seems to characterize many of the simpler behavioral patterns which Lorenz and his followers examined, such as the orientation behaviors or ritualized courtship displays of many bird species.

Unfortunately, Lorenz mechanically extrapolated from this work to suggest that similar principles probably apply to much more complex and variable social behaviors, and (in his 1966 book *On Aggression*) ended up arguing for an innate basis of aggressive behavior in human beings. The ethology literature of this period (Lorenz, Ardrey, Morris, etc.) shares with the more recent sociobiology literature a mechanical reductionist methodology, a tendency to treat even very complex social behaviors as if they were collections of compartmentalized individual behavioral acts, and as if they were necessarily tied to specific genetic programs. Both schools typically underestimate the degree to which genetic programming itself can, in many species, lead to variable behavioral patterns in relation to varying environmental cues, and both share an infuriating tendency to extrapolate from some of the most rigidly patterned behaviors in nature (e.g., Lorenz's birds; Wilson's social insects, etc.) to explain the behaviors found in that species well known by all to be the most dependent on acquired learning and subject to frequent and dramatic nonbiological changes in its social structures: human beings.

and bogs, rather than a truly aquatic form). But Morgan seems convinced that our ancestors were well on their way to becoming a fully aquatic species, complete with specialized aquatic adaptations (while somehow retaining amazing similarities to the terrestrial apes), and then shifted gears again to resume terrestrial life. The impetus for this first transformation was supposedly a "biological emergency" due to droughts, shrinking forests, and the inhospitability of savannas, while the impetus for "reemerging" is left unstated, save for the fact that the rains returned. (Did our ancestors, frolicking in the water for 10 million or so years, just get nostalgic for their roots and decide to go home again at the first sign of overcast skies?)

Well, sorry, it just doesn't work that way. In fact, Morgan's book is so ridiculous that it is tempting to dismiss it easily and toss it into the trash. But it apparently has enjoyed a certain popularity among those who, like Morgan herself, correctly desire to reevaluate the role of females in our early evolution and to debunk the assorted androcentric myths. Unfortunately Morgan's methodology is so flawed that it can only weaken and divert such needed attempts. Consider its main problems.

First, Morgan's entire reconstruction rests on the supposed aquatic phase in our evolution. Knock this down and the whole thing collapses. In addition to the reasons given above, the improbability of this phase comes out in relation to a number of points. Morgan places a great deal of emphasis on the existence of a fossil "gap" of 12 million years or so separating the fossils of presumably ancestral forest-dwelling apes and the first examples of clear hominid fossils. She claims that such a "gap" can only be explained by the hypothesis that our ancestors had become aquatic and left no preservable remains on land. There are a number of problems with this. Aside from the fact that it is not clear why fossil remains would not have appeared in silt deposits of ancient oceans and lakes, Morgan is making the common but unwarranted assumption that major evolutionary changes always take place along a smooth, unbroken continuum and that it should therefore be possible to find a neatly ordered and uninterrupted sequence linking the ancestral apes through the various hominids to modern humans. But gaps, or sharp breaks and discontinuities in fossil sequences of many evolutionary lines, are in fact *real* and in many cases are likely to correspond to qualitative leaps in evolutionary processes: as a basic point of methodology one should resist the tendency to always conceive of large-scale evolutionary change necessarily occurring through a gradual accumulation of minor changes and along a smooth, uninterrupted continuum (cf. Gould and Eldredge 1972). It is, in fact, a generally acknowledged feature of the fossil record that new species often seem to appear rather "abruptly," with numerous fossils appearing where none were previously found. While there continues to be considerable controversy concerning large-scale evolutionary processes such as speciation and extinction,[4] one likely explanation for the "sudden appearance" of a particular species in the fossil record is that a relatively localized speciation event has resulted from rapid changes in relatively small, peripherally isolated populations of the ancestral stock. If this were followed by a massive and rapid radiation or expansion of the new species, it might well seem to "explode" all of a sudden onto the fossil record. Thus, where a clear "link" cannot be established

---

[4]The extent to which they occur gradually and on a smooth continuum or are punctuated by concentrated qualitative leaps separated by relatively long periods of stasis is currently a subject of heated debate (cf. Eldredge and Gould 1972; Gould and Eldredge 1977; Gould 1983 for arguments in favor of a punctuated model of macroevolutionary change).

between a fossil species and presumed immediate ancestors, it may indicate the occurrence of a relatively sudden (in geological terms) major evolutionary leap or divergence. It may also simply reflect the fact that fossils of the most direct ancestors have not yet been found. Interestingly, Richard Leakey and Alan Walker have recently reported a find in Northern Kenya of an apelike fossil dated at 17 million years, which may in fact be a rare representative of a form ancestral to both humans and all the great apes. In any case it should be noted that well-preserved anthropoid fossils going back more than a few million years are not exactly a dime a dozen, and if in fact the Pliocene,[5] during which the ape-human divergence is thought to have taken place, was a period marked by severe climatic changes and a shrinking of forested areas, ancestral forms may well have been subject to extensive population reductions and local extinctions and one might therefore expect an even greater paucity of fossils from that time in a given region.

More importantly, Morgan, writing in 1971, assumes that the hominids diverged from the ancestral tree-dwelling apes a good 10 or 12 million years ago. In the past few years, however, new information has come to light which has led most scientists to believe that the divergence from the apes actually happened much, much more recently—a mere 4 or 5 million years ago. A reexamination of fossil dental remains once thought to be hominid from 5.5 million years ago has led to their being reclassified as ape remains (Ramapithecus, for instance, is no longer generally considered to be on the hominid line); most crucially, a new technique for

---

[5]Morgan's dates for the Pliocene cover about 12 million years, starting about 18 million years ago. The Pliocene is now considered to have been of much shorter duration, extending from about 5 million years ago to about 1.8 million years ago (Tanner 1981, p. 44).

"molecular dating" has been developed which makes it possible to roughly estimate the time when related species alive today would likely have diverged from a common ancestor. This technique, based on assessing the degree of relative similarity in the amino acid sequencing of typical protein chains of two or more related species, provides convincing evidence that our ancestors diverged *in the very recent past* from the ancestral ape stock which also gave rise to the chimpanzees and gorillas. There is a strikingly small difference—less than 1%—in the amino acid sequencing of average human protein molecules and their counterparts in chimpanzees, and this can be calibrated to deduce an estimated divergence time from a common ancestor only 3 to 5 million years ago (for more on this, cf. Tanner 1981, pp. 37-43, and contained references). These dates, deduced from the biochemical makeup of living organisms, correlate well with the evidence obtained from the fossil record: fossils which are clearly hominid have been dated back to some 3 or 4-plus million years ago. If the ape-hominid divergence occurred this recently, there is no basis for suggesting the occurrence of a major gap in the *hominid* line per se.

There is thus no basis whatsoever for Morgan's claim of a hominid aquatic phase, and all the evidence which *is* available points in another direction: the earliest hominid fossils to date have been found in areas which were once mosaic savannas (i.e., grasslands dotted with patches of woodland or clumps of trees), as well as zones of lava flows, bogs, river banks, and gallery forests (strips of forests bordering waterways). All this strongly suggests that the earliest forms diverging from the ancestral apes were exploiting *patchy* terrestrial environments, combinations of open savannas and deeper woodland cover.

It could be argued that Morgan, whose book was published in 1971, cannot be faulted for not knowing much of the information on fossil classification, biochemical dating, and ecological reconstruction, all of which have only emerged in the last few years. But hers is not just a problem of ignorance. It is one thing to engage in speculation, even wild speculation, to generate new ideas in an area as loaded with theoretical dead weight and sociocultural bias as the field of early human evolution. It is fine to range broadly, to shake things up and pose new questions. But it is quite another thing to posit tentative speculation as firm assumptions and then to rig up a whole theory based on these assumptions as if they were hard facts. This is exactly what Morgan does throughout her whole book, and particularly in relation to her "aquatic phase" in the transition from the apes. She builds everything else on this as if it were demonstrably true and without so much as a critical caveat.

This is not just bad science. After constructing her whole scenario in terms of biological evolution, she draws from it a vast assortment of baseless explanations for human social behavior today, focusing especially on the relations between men and women and on the causes of war. Especially because Morgan presents her politically loaded pronouncements as if they were natural consequences of our early biological evolution—leaving aside for now the key question of whether it is even valid to seek explanations of modern human social behavior in processes of *biological* evolution—when her whole evolutionary model is so riddled with false assumptions and absurd storytelling passed off as serious fact, her book can only be described as grotesquely irresponsible, regardless of her intentions. This critique will not attempt to expose every single one of the crude falsehoods in Morgan's work because, quite literally, this writer could find something wrong in almost every sentence of her book. A few examples should suffice to paint the picture.

Forget for the moment that there is ample reason to

doubt her key assumption, that of an aquatic phase in human evolution. How does Morgan set out to test her assumption? By openly looking for features which might "fit" her story and then proclaiming that these features can be explained in light of the initial assumption, thereby "proving" it to be true. She can't possibly lose! So now the classical Tarzanist reconstruction is replaced, by very similar methods, with a reconstruction which runs like this: in diverging from our ape ancestors we evolved the ability to walk on two legs *because* we had to stand in deep water to escape predators after we left the forests; we lost our coat of fur *because* we needed to be streamlined for aquatic life; we put on a layer of subcutaneous fat *because* we needed warmth in the water; our females developed bigger breasts *because* helpless infants needed to get a better reach and handhold in slippery conditions; we kept hair on top of our heads *so* babies could hang on in the water; we evolved a nose over our nostrils *because* we had to protect our sinuses while diving; we developed facial expression *because* we had to squint in the glare of the sun; women got big buttocks *because* they needed to sit comfortably on pebble beaches while nursing babies; the vagina shifted to a more forward position *because* women needed "additional protection against salt water and abrasive sand;" we switched to frontal sex *because* that's the way marine mammals have to do it; we developed control of vocalization as a precursor to speech *because* when we "took to living in the sea, olfactory communication became virtually nonoperative;" etc.; etc.; *ad nauseam*. Of course Morgan interjects a few "possiblys" and "most likelys" here and there, but she keeps weaving the whole fabric of her story as if all the "suggestions" had become indisputable, using phrases like the "only possible explanation is" when perfectly plausible alternative explanations are not even discussed.

The one thing that makes Morgan's book interesting

to this writer is that her little "story" is actually a particularly crude expression of some problems which have marred a lot of "serious" evolutionary biology in the last few decades, and which have become most concentrated and damaging in the methodology of the sociobiologists. For instance, Morgan uses a common form of "shorthand" when dealing with processes of natural selection and evolution which, while admittedly making for less belabored sentences, tends to confer some kind of conscious intent and direction to the processes described (e.g., erect posture evolved because of a need to stand in water to escape predators, etc.). This is a common verbal and written shorthand among many evolutionary biologists. If pressed, they will quickly point out that they only mean that, given a certain amount of genetic variation in a population confronted with a changing environment, particular features conferring a reproductive advantage in a particular situation would tend to increase in the population as a whole, and perhaps become characteristic of the whole species. But the common shorthand style is not only potentially very misleading to those less trained in this field: it also reacts back upon those using the shorthand, serving to muddle their own thinking and to cover up errors and false assumptions.[6]

In Morgan's case it is not simply sloppy technique, but seems in fact to cover up a lot of ignorance about basic evolutionary processes. In places she writes as if all evolutionary change stemmed from single mutations, as if individuals rather than species evolved, as if things had conveniently evolved to fit certain felt "needs," and as if all evolutionary changes were adaptations to environmental strictures.

This latter error is perhaps the most prevalent, both

---

[6]For drawing particular attention to this latter aspect, I am particularly indebted to Bob Avakian (unpublished correspondence).

in Morgan's work and in the evolutionary literature generally. But, again, features are not selected because they are adaptive, and it is therefore not possible to identify some feature, determine (rightfully or not) that it is now adaptive, and, from that, work back and assume it evolved as an adaptation. The most which can be done is to raise the question of whether it is plausibly an adaptation and to look for possible bases and pathways for its evolution, probable developmental constraints, and alternative explanations. Further, there is no biological validity to the reductionist approach which treats every little bit of morphology and behavior as a direct result of natural selection: while natural selection is the most important agent of biological evolutionary change, there are other processes which can lead to evolutionary shifts in populations and species without being directly tied into an increase in the reproductive success of individuals (such as the random fixation of neutral alleles[7] and the random changes in gene frequencies in a population known as "genetic drift," which can occur particularly when the size of a population is dramatically reduced, as when a small number of individuals founds a new, isolated population [cf., for instance, Gould and Lewontin 1979, pp. 590-91]).

Furthermore, many features of organisms are indirectly produced as simple developmental consequences of changes in *other* features subjected to selective forces; this is because natural selection operates on the organism as a whole rather than arbitrarily delin-

---

[7]An allele is one of several alternate forms of a gene occupying the same spot on a chromosome. Random changes in the proportional representation of different alleles in a population may alter the overall composition of the genetic pool and thus the diversity of genetic material available to an interbreeding population—but whether this will or will not have a discernible effect on the survival and reproduction of individuals will depend on the type of alleles involved.

eated parts of its morphology, physiology, or behavior, and because there are historical developmental *constraints* which channel and restrict the pathways of evolutionary change (Gould and Lewontin 1979, p. 594). In some insects, for instance, the yellow coloration of the Malpighian tubules cannot be a direct result of natural selection; since these structures are not visible from the outside to any other organisms, the coloration seems in fact to be simply a *byproduct* of the metabolic reactions which go into producing a red eye pigmentation in these same insects, which may itself be adaptive and have been favored by natural selection. Similarly, the chin, a feature which is more pronounced in humans than in other primates, does not have to have evolved as an adaptation, but is most likely merely a developmental consequence of different rates in the evolutionary reduction of the size of two growth fields in the human face, which may themselves have been more directly subject to selection pressures (Lewontin 1979, p. 7).

Morgan doesn't understand any of this: she treats every characteristic she can identify as if it were a discrete entity evolving in a vacuum, and *as if it were necessarily an adaptation.* She then asks "adaptive for what?," proceeds to make up an adaptive story about why an individual having the genes for such a feature would leave more offspring, and then proclaims: Eureka! *This* is how it evolved. This method guarantees results because you can always make up stories until you find one that could, in retrospect, explain the development of a certain feature, especially if you are not overly concerned with identifying the historical bases and constraints affecting the likelihood of such a change. The problem is that evolutionary change does not operate from a *tabula rasa.* The morphology, physiology, and behavior of a species, its patterns of interaction with other species and with the physical environment—all condition and restrict the evolutionary options open to it. For instance, our arm bones retain features of the arm bones of our ancestors (revealing that they were brachiating apes that moved through trees using their arms), which constituted the raw material from which our arms were modified. Similarly, a new trait will not appear unless some genetic variation for such a trait was present in a population: for instance, the fact that no vertebrates have ever had arms, legs *and* wings does not necessarily mean that such a set-up wouldn't be adaptive; it more likely reflects an absence of the necessary genetic variation for such a trait in the evolutionary history of the vertebrates (Lewontin 1979). Furthermore, natural selection will always favor and spread any feature which leads to an organism leaving more offspring—even if this change turns out to be nonadaptive for the species as a whole (if, for instance, the population increase is not accompanied by a concomitant increase in resources or provokes intensified competition or predation, etc.). Finally, the fact that a feature may be adaptive relative to some environmental stricture *today* does not mean that it evolved originally because it was adaptive in the same way, or at all. This is because life is not static; all interconnected things constantly change; and a feature which was originally a simple developmental consequence of selection for some other feature, or which had itself been shaped by natural selection but in relation to a different function, could at some later time be co-opted, so to speak, and take on a new function for which it had not originally been selected (Gould and Vrba 1982).

Morgan, however, does not even consider the fact that any one feature might have numerous possible explanations, even in terms of natural selection. For instance, all our supposed "aquatic traits" are deemed by her to be so simply because they *could* have been adaptations to an aquatic environment, or because they are similar to certain "typical" features found in marine mammals, etc. But as the great diversity of species of plants and animals encompasses many different morphological, physiological, and behavioral "solutions" to similar environmental necessities, conversely, different species may exhibit very similar features which may nevertheless have very different evolutionary origins, and which may not serve the same specific functions. Nor does natural selection lead or tend to some kind of Perfection of parts or organisms—it is, again, a process of important evolutionary change, in which the characteristics of individuals exhibiting features enhancing survival and reproduction under given conditions will tend to spread and become generalized. This does not mean, however, that the change being incorporated represents the "best possible solution" to "a problem."

Actually, most if not all of Morgan's supposed "aquatic traits" in humans could be explained much more plausibly as consequences of evolution by neotony. The theory of neoteny (cf., for instance, Gould 1977, pp. 63-75) suggests that the evolution of humans was effected through a process of retention of many of the juvenile characteristics of the ancestral species, occurring in conjunction with a reduction in the rate of overall development of individuals. Such a process could explain why human beings are morphologically more similar to the juveniles—rather than to the adults—of other primates, exhibiting longer periods of juvenility than any other mammal, delayed sexual maturity, postnatal brain expansion, and a greater flexibility and capacity to learn than any other primate. The capacity for the retention of juvenile features in forms diverging from the ancestral apes could have been selected for and generalized broadly because morphological changes in the position of the spine, the late-closing skull sutures, etc., would have probably resulted both in an increased capacity for erect posture and bipedality and in potential for greater learning capacity and behavioral flexibility.

As we shall see, these would have conferred a distinct reproductive advantage in any number of environments, and especially in changing environments. Given the likely conditions in which our ancestors diverged from the ancestral apes (a time of significant climatic and topographic changes, and an apparent move into environments such as savannas, which are characterized by patchy resource distributions, high unpredictability, etc.), it seems very probable that phenotypic rigidity under such circumstances would have led to extinction.

But is the theory of evolution by neoteny just another "adaptive story" along lines similar to Morgan's aquatic theory? Perhaps, but almost certainly not. Neoteny is not simply a more plausible interpretation of the evolutionary processes involved in the divergence, encompassing both the ancestral material basis available to begin with *and* the particular distinguishing features which are demonstrably present in *Homo sapiens* relative to our closest living ape relatives (the morphological differences, greater flexibility, longer life, greater capacity for learning, etc.). The theory of neoteny is also supported by the fact that many seemingly puzzling features of human beings are found in juveniles or embryos of other primates or mammals, but not in the adults of these species. Among these features are the relative hairlessness; the rounded cranium; the proportionally smaller jaw; the positioning of the foramen magnum (the hole in the skull which is the entry point for the spine) underneath the skull, as in the embryos of quadrupedal mammals, rather than behind it, as in the fully developed forms of these species; the late closure of skull sutures, allowing for postnatal brain expansion; the ventral positioning of the vagina, a feature shared by all mammalian embryos in their early stages of development; the unrotated big toe of the foot, also a primate embryonic feature, and one which makes for poor climbing but better walking; etc. Thus there is much which suggests that the Naked Ape is really more like a primate embryo or juvenile than a specialized aquatic mammal. Given all this and given who our ancestors were, and given the fact that we are still extremely closely related to the present-day African apes, there is really no reason to invoke aquatic specialization as a trend in our early history.

As for Morgan's particular concern with the origins of human females' larger breasts and buttocks relative to the apes, she is correct to point out that there is no reason to believe that such features evolved in order to sexually entice and satisfy hominid males, and to thereby reinforce tight pair-bonds between males and females (as is commonly asserted in the popular Tarzanist literature). But it is just as unlikely that these features evolved as handgrips for babies, padding for sitting on beaches, or wet-suit insulation! It is quite possible that, at least at first, these features emerged simply as associated developmental consequences of morphological changes associated with walking on two legs (the musculature of the buttocks is associated with the maintenance of erect posture in both sexes and the subcutaneous layer of fat would not only serve to preserve heat in cold water—the *only* possibility Morgan finds conceivable—but could also be of use in arid environments and in environments where food sources are scarce and unreliable, as fatty tissue can store water and various nutrients). Compared to the rain forest environments apparently inhabited by our most distant ape ancestors, mosaic savannas are hot and dry; the palatable leaves, roots, insects, and small animals which likely constituted our ancestors' diet (before the emergence of sophisticated weapon use and the capacity to digest greater amounts of meat) would have been relatively scarce and scattered. Both sexes would have benefited from an extra layer of fat under such conditions, but it may well have become more pronounced in females who were subject to greater nutritional stresses due to pregnancy and prolonged periods of nursing and infant dependency.

Similar alternative explanations can be suggested for just about every one of Morgan's supposed "aquatic traits," and this is in large part why Morgan's book is so useless. The point here is not to go after every example, but to give the reader a sense of how fundamentally flawed Morgan's whole *approach* is. And the rest of her book—her reconstruction of hominid evolution after their supposed reemergence from the water in the Pleistocene, and especially her notions of changes in *social behavior* at that time and their supposed implications for modern-day society—are all based on this rotten scaffolding. Morgan intended to inject a fresh perspective on the role of women in early human evolution in order to counter the standard Tarzanist chauvinism of the orthodox reconstructions; ironically, save for the fact that she considers, quite plausibly, that transitional hominid females were likely to have been the source of many key behavioral innovations, including tool use, most of Morgan's story is just as scientifically perverted and ultimately harmful as that of the Tarzanists it sets out to discredit.

Consider the question of human sexuality: while she correctly discounts and ridicules the common unsubstantiated assumptions that women's breasts and buttocks, the loss of estrus,[8] and the switch to ventral sex all developed "for the pleasure of man" and "the

---

[8]Estrus in other mammalian females refers to periodic physiological and behavioral manifestations which correspond to the times females can become pregnant, and which serve as "clues" to the males of female sexual availability and interest. In other primate females, estrus is accompanied by olfactory signals, clearly visible genital swellings, changes in coloration, etc., indicating times of peak fertility.

better to cement pair-bonds when the men went off hunting" etc., Morgan replaces this with the idea that our imagined aquatic phase is the root of a whole gamut of sexual maladjustments which plague humanity and which have turned us into the "crazy mixed-up creatures" we supposedly are today. Morgan's basic idea here is that we were well on our way to becoming fully adapted to a marine environment and that when we came back out we were burdened with incomplete adaptations in a different setting. In particular, we had switched to frontal sex as opposed to the more common rear-mounting method prevalent among other primates and the mammals generally. In fact, frontal sex probably increasingly became the preferred position as the location of the vagina was shifting to a more forward location, making rear access more difficult. While there is no reason to believe this shift in favored approach created any serious problems for the evolving hominids, to Morgan it represents the beginning of all our problems, the source of "an *innate* predisposition to anxiety" in both sexes (Morgan's italics) and of particular misery for the females who were supposedly saddled with a body no longer apt to give them much sexual pleasure. (Morgan postulates reduced vaginal stimulation in the new position, and as for the role of the clitoris in female orgasm, well, she thinks the clitoris probably evolved for a different purpose and is not yet fully adapted to its new role and that *this*—rather than any kind of sociocultural factors—is why many women don't experience orgasm. To this one can only say, give us a break!)

The initial source of all tensions between men and women resides, according to Morgan, in what we might refer to as the "Primeval Rape Scene" (my choice of words), which runs as follows:

> When we left our pair of aquatic apes, she was presenting her posterior to him in the gesture of sex-

ual invitation employed by primates for millions of years....

...But she picked the wrong ape. He was one of the pioneer types, like the one who first killed a seal and the one who first flaked a pebble, and the promethean genius that lit the first fire. In the field of frontal sex, as in all these other cases, there must have been a time when it had never happened before. Instead of responding in a proper and friendly fashion, he threw her on to her back....

...[N]othing had prepared our aquatic anthropoid for what was happening to her now, being flung down on the shingle on her soft wet hairless back and mounted the wrong way up....

...She thought he had gone berserk and was aiming to disembowel her....

...Dizzy with terror, she was only aware that at the hands of this absolute beginner her viscera were being squashed and the air compressed out of her lungs—and *that* had never happened in an amatory context to any quadruped, reptile or mammal, since the world began....

Generally speaking, in the primate world, sex is a purely functional affair. He knew by his sense of smell she was biologically ready for him; he knew by her "presenting" posture that she was psychologically ready for him; and yet here she was perversely kicking up this frightful din and pretending the whole thing had been *his* idea. It's hardly probable that he would instantly react with friendly persuasion. It was far more likely to make him hate her guts. Indeed, I'm convinced his sex has never felt quite the same about ours from that day to this. (Morgan 1971, pp. 65-69)

The rest is history.

The outpouring of festering subjectivity in this section of Morgan's book is truly mind-boggling. Never mind the facts. Never mind, for instance, the fact that frontal sex seems to occur fairly frequently in the higher primates, including among some of our very closest living relatives, the pygmy chimpanzees, *Pan paniscus* (Savage-Rumbaugh and Wilkerson 1978, pp. 335-36). Never mind that the females among them, as well as the males, often initiate copulation, that copulation is accompanied by much exploration, handling of genitals, nonverbalized communication, physiological arousal of the female clitoris, and reactions which resemble for all the world female orgasm. And never mind that in the higher primates, such as chimpanzees, mating behavior (just as maternal care of young and a lot of other complex social interactions) has to be *learned*—that it is not directly genetically programmed—and that individuals who are deprived of social contact since birth have no idea what to do when placed among other individuals of their species. Such things suggest that early hominids may well have increasingly favored frontal sex because of morphological changes making it more convenient for both sexes, and that some form of communication and learning played an important role in sexual encounters early on. But to Morgan the Primeval Rape set an ugly, violent precedent from which we have yet to recover, and the basic problems between men and women today lie not in prevailing social relations, but in some faulty biological manufacturing. It is painfully ironic that a feminist, supposedly concerned with combating the oppression of women, should go through such forced contortions to come up with yet another biodeterminist schema which necessarily severely limits the possibilities for change in human societies, including in the relations between men and women. Luckily for those of us who don't particularly like the present order of things, all of history points to prevailing social relations rather than innate constraints in our biological makeup as the key factor mediating every aspect of human social life at different points of history and in different parts of the globe. A key point which will be addressed later in this

book is that *our biology itself,* geared towards unprecedented behavioral flexibility, provides a key to
understanding why this is so.

But for Morgan, even the absence of clear estrus
cycles in human females becomes reason enough to
believe that relations between men and women have
historically been warped because of fundamental,
biologically grounded maladaptations going back to our
earliest origins. She believes that hominid females were
early deprived of "behavioral rewards" for sexual activity because sex had become less pleasurable for them
(see above); therefore, reasons Morgan, hominid females
would no longer have had any incentive to advertise
peak periods of sexual interest by going into estrus,
which would invite males to mate. In time, all visible
signs of estrus would disappear.

This view is just as fanciful as the standard Tarzanist
notion that estrus was lost because natural selection
favored a system in which females would be perpetually
sexually available, thereby ensuring that a given male
would have some incentive to hang around a particular
female and to provide for her and her young on an ongoing basis; thus the rise of the tight monogamous pair-
bonds which the Tarzanists usually consider to be the
bedrock of human society. Morgan sees the loss of estrus
as resulting from females rejecting sex, the Tarzanists as
resulting from females more consistently indulging
males—two sides of the same coin. In reality there is a
basis neither for Morgan's assumption of a biologically
mediated loss of sexual interest in females nor for the
Tarzanist suggestion that the possibility of females
mating during more extended periods would draw them
into tight pair-bonds with one male (why not many?). Indeed, estrus does not serve as a specific signal of sexual
"interest" but as an external indication of *ovulation*
(and therefore ability to become pregnant). There is in
fact recent and well-documented evidence that higher

primate females (including our close relatives, the pygmy chimpanzees) commonly mate outside of estrus, and at their own initiative. Therefore an estrus cycle advertising ovulation (and perhaps secondarily an increase in sexual interest) is not incompatible with extended periods of sexual interest and activity.

In recent years there has been a flurry of interest in the estrus question (especially among sociobiologists) due to its possible social implications for the relations between men and women. The absence of estrus in human females is often described in terms of the supposed evolution of "concealed ovulation" (cf. Burley and other references cited in Hrdy 1981, pp. 140-43). Typically the problem is posed in this form: why would it have been adaptive (i.e., ultimately reproductively advantageous) for hominid females to evolve the capacity to conceal from males, and even from themselves, the precise time at which they could become pregnant? Explanations have included the idea that the loss of estrus removed any remaining restrictions on copulation outside the time of ovulation, thereby enabling females to mate frequently and with multiple males and to draw these males into helping to care for the young, which (precise timing of ovulation being concealed) they would "all of them [have] some probability of having sired" (Hrdy 1981, p. 157); the notion that concealed ovulation would enable the females to trick males into staying around longer, since those who didn't might miss the time of ovulation and father fewer young; and the idea that natural selection operated to conceal ovulation not only from the males but from the females themselves, when, with the development of human consciousness, women sought to avoid or limit pregnancies due to fear of pain or death. In this latter view, natural selection would have tended to *counter* this seemingly biologically maladaptive tendency by depriving women of the knowledge of precise timing of ovulation (for a more complete explanation of these various hypotheses, cf. Hrdy 1981, pp. 140-43, and especially contained references).

While this book cannot attempt to discuss and criticize these various theories in detail, it should be pointed out that they all treat the absence of estrus as if it had necessarily evolved as an adaptation, and they all tend to blur the lines between the biological origins of the phenomenon and its possible derived implications for human or hominid social structures and culturally instituted forms of relations between the sexes (e.g., family structures). There may be bits and pieces of truth in some of these theories in terms of the social repercussions of the absence of estrus (it may in fact have facilitated more ongoing continuous relationships of a female with one or more males and reduced competition between males for females in heat, thus contributing to a more low-key social climate overall, which in turn might have led to more stable bands, increased male care of the young, and/or reduced tendencies of the males to kill the young of other males, common in the higher primates, etc.). But even if some of these features were the consequences of the initial loss of estrus (and it is not clear that they were), this says little of the origins of the change. Perhaps there never was an "evolution of concealed ovulation." Perhaps it was simply a byproduct of some other evolutionary change. The literature keeps asking over and over again: how was this change adaptive? We should at least entertain the thought that it may never have been an adaptation.

But even if it was overall the result of selection, one has to ask what possible reproductive advantage in the long or short term can be derived from the loss of signals externally advertising the prime time for fertilization to take place. In mammals generally, estrus cycles may well have initially been selected for if individuals exhibiting clear signs of ovulation also engaged in the most productive matings at the peak of fertility. Again, this would not necessarily preclude matings at other times (as in the higher primates), but it would practically guarantee that mating would take place in fertile times. But this only works if there is a very high degree of correlation between the estrus signs and the actual time of ovulation (as indeed there seems to be in mammals with estrus cycles). A well-known fact that has even been stressed in some of the literature on "concealed ovulation" (cf. Burley, cited in Hrdy 1981, pp. 143, 229) is that the reproductive cycle in human females, compared to that of other mammalian females, is on the whole extremely irregular (which explains, for instance, the consistent failure of the rhythm method of contraception). There are significant variations in the length of menstrual intervals and the days of ovulation within that. Furthermore, it is a well-documented fact that in modern women ovulation and menstruation often cease altogether for extended periods of time in situations of extreme nutritional stress or outright starvation (e.g., Frisch 1978, pp. 22, 24).

Isn't it therefore possible that as the ancestral ape populations moved into more unpredictable, resource-scarce environments, the regularity of the ovulation cycles may have been disrupted and have fluctuated with the available food supplies? If ovulation cycles were frequently disrupted, the estrus cycles might often have been out of sync with ovulation in the period of the initial divergence of the hominids from the apes, and may no longer have coordinated mating with ovulation quite as faithfully. If such were the case, it is likely that individual females who did *not* exhibit clear signs of estrus, and the males who would mate with such females, would have mated more often and therefore have been more likely to hit the right timing in relation to ovulation and have left more offspring, thereby perpetuating the trend. While it should be stressed that this author is here engaging only in speculation, as both the reasons for the absence of estrus in humans and its social implications require further investigation, this suggested scenario seems at least plausible and in keeping with basic laws of evolutionary change. It is, however, in sharp contrast to the preferred speculations of the Tarzanists or of the sociobiologists—and this in itself should cause one to reflect on a methodology which almost always assumes that biological features having social repercussions are rooted in the presumed evolution of these features as adaptations *specifically geared to* producing these social changes.

And as long as we're engaging in a bit of imaginative speculation and suggesting alternative explanations here, consider Morgan's idea of the "evolution" of female menopause (the cessation of ovulation and menstruation in women, which marks the end of a few decades of fertility). This phenomenon seems to be absent in other mammalian females, including other primates. A common view is that this feature "evolved" by natural selection as an adaptation which protected females from the dangers of childbearing in their later years. But to assume selection "for" menopause on this basis requires an assumption that the reproductive potential of individual females was somehow increased by their continuing to live and consume food and other resources (perhaps depriving their own offspring of these) long past the point of being able to bear young— which is unlikely, to say the least. Morgan tackles this problem with an approach which is typical these days among sociobiologists: by confusing levels of selection and by blurring over distinctions between biologically programmed factors and cultural factors in human societies. She categorically states that "the only way of accounting for the evolutionary emergence of the menopause in women" is to assume that this was of benefit "to the tribe as a whole" because older sterile females would be valuable as "repositories of wisdom" (in areas of child care and doctoring, for instance, while old men might be stores of hunting lore). Thus, in Morgan's view, a "menopausal mutation" would be "adaptive for the species as a whole" and would be favored by natural selection.

First of all, there are a number of obvious errors here, such as the unsubstantiated assumption of a single mutation, the notion of selection operating directly at the level of the group rather than at the level of individuals, and the idea of selection as a mechanism geared specifically to adaptation. But even if the argument were rephrased more carefully in terms of selection operating at the level of individuals—i.e., by suggesting that the presence of elderly females in some way increased the survival and reproductive potential of their direct progeny and very closely related individuals—this argument would still fail to recognize that, while older women and men are indeed objectively valuable to human societies as living repositories of historical knowledge, *a genetic reconstruction would not be necessary* to ensure their survival past their reproductive years. The reason for this is precisely that human beings early on evolved the capacity for culture and cultural transmission— and that *this* is the sphere through which all social decisions are made in human societies, including whether to cherish and support, or neglect and dispose of, society's elderly.[9]

Stephen Jay Gould has similarly criticized a favorite sociobiological explanation for the phenomenon, among

---

[9]In this light it is interesting to note that fossil remains of Neandertal hominids from about 50,000 years ago reveal a surprisingly high incidence of old people, an apparently common long life span of about 50 years, and the presence of some severely crippled individuals, all of which suggests that individuals in Neandertal societies were cared for when unable to provide for themselves.

certain nomadic Eskimo peoples, of old people voluntarily staying behind to die in times of food scarcity rather than endanger others by slowing them down. Because these nomadic peoples are organized around groups of closely related individuals, the sociobiologists love to suggest that this is evidence for selection of "altruistic genes," reasoning that the elders who sacrifice themselves will leave more descendants and thereby increase the spread of their genes. Gould has pointed out that the very same phenomenon can be explained much more plausibly in terms of cultural evolution: such a tradition of sacrificing could in fact emerge and be popularized, and may well have been in fact "very adaptive" in various circumstances, without ever having to have been genetically programmed, if families without such traditions were unlikely to survive (Gould 1977, p. 256). And again, on the question of menopause, it is important to remember that it may never have been a direct adaptation at all; it could perhaps have been a simple developmental consequence of evolution by neoteny and overall retarded development. Humans are distinguished by their prolonged juvenility, delayed sexual maturation, and longer life spans relative to other primates: timewise, it is as if everything had been stretched out, although not always to the same degree. It may well be that the cessation of ovulation in primates is an early physiological sign of aging, but that in most primates it is not recognizable as "menopause" simply because individuals rarely live past that point, whereas in humans with stretched-out life spans it may be followed by decades of healthy living. Thus menopause may not indicate any specific genetic reconstruction but may simply be an attendant consequence of the prolonged lives typical of the human species. And it should be obvious that, in addition to any possible biological basis, the development of material surpluses would have furthered this trend even more—today many signs of senescence (physiological aging) accompany us through many years of our lives (greying hair, loss of visual acuity or hearing, loss of muscle tone, etc.), most of which need not have much effect on our activities or social relations exactly because of the primacy of sociocultural factors in unleashing or restricting all that we do.

But Morgan goes on and on along her biodeterminist track, focusing on human sexual relations as the hub of the world's ills. She spins off tales of how the Primeval Rape led to loss of estrus, frequent absence of orgasm in women, and even to females being repulsed by male bodies. This gets to the point where she makes the remarkable statement that, to women, male penises are "not very pretty," and that this is due to "a prolonged evolutionary stage in which its associations were more disturbing than delightful" (p. 144). Thanks, but no thanks, Queen Victoria! Aside from the fact that a very great number of women around the world would contest these sentiments, it is really quite amazing that in a species so dependent on knowledge acquired through learning as our own, Morgan could ignore the role of culture and social stratification to such an extent.

Having told us that the origin of the oppression of women is biologically grounded in the Primeval Rape, Morgan moves on to a similar treatment of the question of aggression. Just like her foes among the pop anthropologists and the more modern sociobiologists, Morgan sets out to reveal the origins of modern aggression and war in our early biological evolution, suggesting an innate biological basis for social conflicts. The fact that there is no evidence whatsoever that any human social behavior is genetically programmed—and lots of reasons for thinking such programming highly unlikely (more on this later)—never seems to bother Morgan any more than it does the assorted Tarzanists and sociobiologists whose garbage assaults us daily. Morgan's only particularity is to place the origin of aggression back at the

Primeval Rape scene, a time when (according to her) it would have been reproductively advantageous for males to drop any previously evolved "restraints" on aggressive behavior, since such restraints could only get in the way of successful impregnation of those recalcitrant females.[10]

There is in fact very little validity to even the use of the term "aggression" to describe both a wide range of confrontational behaviors in various species of animals *and* what is termed aggression in human beings. As R. C. Lewontin has justly pointed out:

> Some sociobiologists now wish us to believe that human political aggression and human individual aggression are transformations of the same phenomenon, general animal aggression. Thus, war becomes a manifestation of human nature, the inbuilt aggression in all of us that must be artificially controlled if the species is to be at peace. But a few moments' reflection shows that people do not march off to wars because they feel aggressive toward each other, although governments attempt to instill such feelings after the fact as a tactic in war. . . . Political aggression derives from political and economic causes, not

---

[10]Morgan refers to a suggestion by Konrad Lorenz that species of animals which in the course of their evolution have relied more on evasion and flight than on direct encounters for dealing with potential threats may never have evolved either ritualized fighting or the other behaviors which substitute for all-out fights to the death in many species that do engage in direct encounters with other individuals. Lorenz further suggests that species which had not evolved such restraints might exhibit inordinately aggressive behavior when individuals were forced into direct encounters by new conditions, a pattern he observed in caged ring doves. Whether or not such developments could ever have marked the hominid populations which diverged from the apes, the later development of culture would in any case have quickly superceded whatever genetically based grounding for aggression there might once have been.

from gut feelings of territoriality, xenophobia and aggression. The conflation by sociobiologists of the two meanings of aggression in a single explanatory attempt is obfuscating. The same conflation exists between the animal and human meanings of territoriality and hierarchy.... [I]t tends to mask the commodity nature of human slavery and its use for the production of economic surplus rather than for subsistence." (Lewontin 1979, p. 8)

For Morgan, however, it is sufficient to claim that our ancestors had big canine teeth and therefore must have been aggressive. From this she deduces behavioral restraints, which later must have been "dropped" when it became reproductively advantageous to do so—with the switch to frontal mating when "he violently threw her on to her back." Never mind that Morgan's definition of aggression is couched in descriptions of physiological reactions which are equally applicable to fighting or to running away (adrenalin rushes, etc.); and never mind that the fossil record indicates a marked reduction in the size of the canine teeth of the earliest hominids relative to the apes, long before the development of weapons as substitutes for teeth. Never mind, too, that there is just no basis to assume that the ancestral apes were particularly "aggressive": if they were similar to the forest-dwelling chimpanzees of today, our closest relatives, they were probably characterized by highly mobile groupings of fluctuating size unlikely to exhibit strict social hierarchies[11] (more on this later). Ignoring

---

[11]Fluid, easily changing associations between individuals are certainly the most commonly recorded in chimpanzee communities. However, Jane Goodall's long-term observations of chimpanzee communities have recently recorded unusual instances of unexpectedly extreme antagonistic interactions between two different populations of chimps which had originally constituted a single group. When the original group split in two, both subgroups

all evidence which could run counter to her thesis, Morgan asks us to believe that in the distant past, long before the emergence of material surpluses and of property relations which would permeate all social relations including those between men and women, a Primeval

---

continued to occupy a fairly restricted geographical area. Terms such as "warfare" and "gang attacks" have been freely bandied about to refer to some bone-breaking, flesh-tearing encounters between the two groups (resulting in some deaths) and much has been made of the fact that a particular adult female captured and killed three, and possibly ten, babies of other females over a four-year period (interestingly, this female's daughter joined her in these attacks and killings but did not continue the practice after the mother's death, suggesting that she was killing by learning and imitation). The revelations that normally quite docile chimps can kill have alternately bolstered those who are convinced that human "aggression" and "warfare" has a deeply rooted biological basis and shaken those who sought in our closest relatives some idealized portrait of noble-savage innocence. Aside from the usual problem with making any kind of direct extrapolation from the social behavior of any other species to our own, Goodall et al.'s observations actually reinforce the view that chimps are themselves capable of a range of social behaviors which vary with varying conditions. That such killings are rare among chimps generally is suggested by the fact that no observations of such behavior were made during the first 14 years that this particular population was under intense scrutiny by Goodall and her associates. By the time this behavior was first observed, three generations of these chimps had become accustomed to ongoing human presence and had been regularly provisioned with stocks of bananas to encourage their staying in close proximity to the research camp, a factor which encouraged the congregation of large numbers of individuals and greatly affected their social interactions. It is thus generally acknowledged (including by Goodall) that these chimps constitute a somewhat unnatural community. Under such disrupting artificial conditions, observations of animal behavior are useful for revealing what those animals are capable of under a certain set of conditions, but this is of limited use in trying to understand the structure and functioning of natural communities. In addition to the host of usual and more fundamental problems referred to in this book, this is one more reason to steer away from anthropomorphic interpretations of such data and extrapolations to human social behaviors.

Rape occurred, and that therein lies the downfall of humanity.

And it goes on and on: wars stem from male bonding and male associations, which emerged with the development of weapons and organized hunting and protection of the groups from predators. Males excelled at this, according to Morgan, because, while female primates congregate for grooming, etc., there is a "real, universal and indisputable difference between cohorts of males and groups of females: namely, that the males are more aggressive" (p. 194). This could even be disputed in many primate species, especially those having fluid social structures; but for human beings, who are extreme among mammals for their lack of sexual dimorphism [12]

---

[12]Sexual dimorphism in a species refers to marked differences between the males and the females of the species in characteristics such as size, strength, special "attention-getting" features such as the male peacock's tail, etc. Such differences are usually thought to be the product of sexual selection for features which augment the reproductive success of individuals in their competition for mates with individuals of the same sex and/or which serve to better attract individuals of the opposite sex. Classical examples of sexual dimorphism apparently resulting from sexual selection include the great difference in weight between male and female stellar sea lions (the male weighs three times as much as the female and the biggest males mate the most because they are able to establish and defend "mating territories" visited by the females), or the bright plumage of many male birds (which often plays an important role in courtship and attracting females).

In some mammals, marked anatomical differences between the sexes are correlated with marked behavioral differences. Savanna baboon males, for instance, are much bigger than the females (twice as big) and have larger canine teeth; these differences are correlated with behavioral differences, as the males are involved in much fighting to set up strict dominance hierarchies among themselves and to repel predators. By contrast, chimpanzees and humans are striking among mammals for their almost complete absence of sexual dimorphism (for instance, females are typically 83 to 95 percent of the weight and length of males in both species, and neither sex has any specialized character-

and who rely so heavily on learned information for their every activity, the statement is preposterous!

Similar statements abound in the sociobiological literature. E.O. Wilson writes, "The average temperamental differences between the human sexes are also consistent with the generalities of mammalian biology. Women as a group are less assertive and physically aggressive" (Wilson 1978, p. 128). In a book in which she seeks to reconcile feminism with sociobiology, Sarah Blaffer Hrdy argues that females in many primate species are aggressive and highly competitive in their own right, and that there is therefore every reason to believe that human females can hold their own just as well as men in highly competitive spheres of activity (Hrdy 1981, see especially pp. 59-71, 96-130). Aside from the applicability of Lewontin's criticism of the tendency of sociobiologists to conflate the terminology of animal behaviors and vastly different human social phenomena to which the same words are ascribed (see above), both these views miss the point: neither men nor women are innately aggressive, any more than either are innately passive—they are all capable of a wide range of emotions and behaviors which are brought forth in response to

---

istics suggesting a basis for greater "dominance" or "aggressiveness"). In discussing sexual dimorphism, Tanner (1981, pp. 200-201, 271-72) reports also that the typical primate "fighting teeth" (the canines) are relatively large in both living and fossil apes as compared to modern humans, and are smaller and less variable in modern humans than in the early hominid fossils. In other words, it seems that there has been an evolutionary trend towards a reduction in the size of the canine teeth in the hominid line, and in fact this trend was well underway even before the emergence of weapons, as pointed out earlier. Of further interest is the suggestion that the greater variability observed in the size of fossil hominid canines may indicate that the evolutionary trend has also been towards a reduction of sexual dimorphism relative to this feature: human canine teeth are not only small, they are also small in *both* sexes.

varying social factors.

A human being *learns* to welcome certain events, individuals, social structures, etc., and to hate others; and prevailing standards of "right" and "wrong" vary in accordance with prevailing social relations. Some people will fight and die to preserve institutions which others will fight and die to get rid of—how then is it possible to talk of a single undifferentiated entity known as "aggression" or "competition" in human beings? And how could such varied responses in a single species be thought to be under specific genetic programming? If indeed they are not, then any differences in so-called assertiveness, competition, aggression, etc., between the sexes are the product of cultural factors. There is probably not a single human society on earth today where differential treatment of boys and girls, from earliest infancy, does not encourage behavioral differences between the sexes, even when attempts are consciously made to minimize this. This is not because of some genetic predisposition towards these behaviors, but because no society is yet free of a division of labor characterized by social inequality, including along sexual lines.

While our complex and ever-changing social relations have long since ceased to be grounded in our biological origins, it is also interesting to note that sex-related behavioral differences may have been minimal in our early hominid ancestors, contrary to the expectations of the sociobiologists. That social structures without strict dominance relations between the sexes are possible among higher primates is clear from the relatively fluid social structures of chimpanzee troops (as opposed to the strictly hierarchical savanna baboons, for instance). Furthermore the degree of sexual dimorphism in human beings (and chimpanzees) is actually strikingly *small*, especially as compared to other mammals—a fact which suggests that at the time of our earliest origins males and females may also have been only minimally dimorphic.

Although Elaine Morgan's book was written a few years before the rampant spread of sociobiological thinking in evolutionary biology (and Morgan's current views on this controversial discipline are not known to this author), her methodology has unavoidably led her to some of the same conclusions, including to the suggestion of an innate basis for current differences between the sexes. "War is a function of male bonding," writes Morgan (p. 204), because males are driven to concoct enemies—real or imagined—to ensure group cohesiveness (in the old days they'd get together to fight leopards, today nations) and "this is the way men are built, and this is the psychological mechanism that powers most of their political systems" (p. 201). One finds no hint here that the causes of war in today's world might be political rivalries between economic formations rooted in commodity production, the existence of class distinctions, and the economic exploitation and political oppression of huge sections of humanity.

Even though Morgan wrote her book at the height of the Vietnam War and was obviously anxious to oppose that war, one would never know that all wars are not equal, or that history is full of examples of women actively engaging in wars—and not always for the worst reasons. As far as Morgan is concerned, women just don't have the right hormones and evolutionary background for this. Again, thanks, but no thanks. Where women have played little role in initiating wars, or have proven to be less than enthusiastic participants, it had everything to do with the general suppression of their initiative in all important spheres and with the fact that these wars did not bode well for the future emancipation of women or the oppressed generally. But the fierce combatant women of the Paris Commune or the women who fought in the numerous wars of national liberation of oppressed nations are among the many examples which put Morgan's thesis to shame and reveal its reactionary nature, and are one more sharp illustration of the bankruptcy of all these biodeterminist theories.

Everything in our early biological evolution—the likely social structures of our ape ancestors, the lack of dimorphism between men and women, the species' early reliance on learning, and the ability to react flexibly to a variety of conditions—all cut against the idea of biologically based, strictly divergent behaviors and capacities between men and women. Since the general oppression of women has nevertheless been an undeniable fact for thousands of years and up through the present, we are compelled to seek its origins in the nonbiological bases for social behavior, to uncover what factors permit and mediate social distinctions and unequal relations in human societies. The key to this is an understanding of the process of accumulation of material surpluses.

This point will be explored later, but it should be noted here that Morgan's neglect of this question blinds her to the full implications of some of her own insights. While recognizing that the use of tools for gathering food (carrying it to different places, storing it, sharing it, etc.) was a key innovation which probably preceded and overshadowed the importance of hunting, she writes as if this had precious little effect on early human social relations, save that they all ate better and that the males must have started increasingly hanging around the females who were likely to have been the first to engage in systematic gathering of food. Because she is blind to the implications of the developing basis for generating a surplus of resources, she is unable to counter the Tarzanists who argue that the nuclear family and monogamy stem from the "fact" that reinforced male-female pair-bonds were required to assure Man the Hunter of appropriate sexual rewards upon his return with the bacon. The best Morgan can muster about the nuclear family is that she believes "its evolution had more to do with economics than with sex" (p. 175), and she then proceeds to muddle up this glimmer of truth by portraying early hominid males as idle loafers who hung around females and the young to get snacks the females had gathered up—and who then had the gall to get cocky and possessive to boot![13]

It is not surprising then, that Morgan's political program (which is tacked on to the end of her book) is less than inspiring. She does not fundamentally question the capitalist social system under which she lives but simply raises objections to some of its excesses.[14]

---

[13]I will return later to the question of the probable basis for the emergence of male dominance, monogamy, and the nuclear family in light of what is known or can plausibly be reconstructed about the earliest hominid societies, and in light of a fuller understanding of the probable dramatic social repercussions of the advent of an ability to gather surplus food above and beyond what was needed for immediate individual consumption and of the resultant capacity for cultural evolution which would come to far outstrip processes of biological evolution as a means for change in the human species. Morgan's failure to grapple with these questions leaves her completely unable to further probe and uncover the bases for social inequalities in human societies, including in the relations between men and women.

[14]At the same time Morgan actually suggests in passing that the Soviet Union is a place where "women have had economic equality for a long time now" and where "equality between the sexes has gone furthest"! Such favorable comments about the Soviet Union are not really surprising, even though, with capitalist commodity relations having long been reinstated in the Soviet Union, Soviet society is of a decidedly nonrevolutionary character and represents no radical departure from the basic social relations prevalent in the capitalist countries of the Western bloc, certainly including the sphere of sexual inequalities! It is, in fact, fairly common for individuals who are merely reform-oriented to be drawn to the tokenistic (and thoroughly false) proclamations of social equality with which the Soviet system still attempts to adorn what are in fact exploitative and oppressive relations.

Morgan even thinks that the protesting youth of the 1960s, while a source of hope, "reject, I personally believe, too much" (p. 207). She feels women should support each other, in whatever endeavor, no matter how narrow. "[W]hat on earth is wrong with being house-proud if that's what turns you on?," she writes (p. 240). One is inclined to answer that what's wrong is that being tied to hearth and home is a concentration of the crippling limitations imposed on the great majority of women throughout the world, and beyond that there are objectively much bigger things going on in the world from which women should not stand aloof, including the growing threat of world war, as well as perhaps unprecedented opportunities for fundamental social change on a world scale. But Morgan merely calls for some patch-up reforms (increased childcare, etc.), and hopes that women will help to devise "cultural curbs" on the men's innate aggression in order to halt wars.

And finally, she hits us with the clincher: thanks to the Pill, says Morgan, "woman is beginning to get her finger on the genetic trigger" (p. 250), because she is able to exercise much finer discrimination in choosing with whom to have children. Morgan speculates wildly that women with broader interests might unfortunately even end up "selecting themselves out" by not having children and that the population of women might come to increasingly be composed of the "descendants of grandmothers and great-grandmothers so fizzing with estrogen that a baby meant more to them than almost any other objective in life" (Morgan, p. 248)—as if breadth or narrowness of outlook and love of children was somehow genetically passed on, and under hormonal control! Morgan can't quite see her way out of her own fantasies at this point and is not quite sure where it will all lead. She concludes that, in any case, women's new ability to control their own reproduction means that "the process of husband-selecting might for the first time begin to have some genetic significance" (p. 249).

There is only one word to describe this genetic trigger stuff: SICK. Morgan's faulty assumptions about the basis and mode of operation of natural selection and her lack of understanding of the primacy of nongenetic, non-inherited, cultural factors in human social relations have led her to the very same kind of thinking which is at the heart of the Tarzanists and of their updated counterparts in sociobiology who, regardless of intent, are among the most sophisticated apologists for the preservation of the status quo in their assumption of the innate biological basis of human social behavior (with its implicit conclusion "so don't bother to change it"). This thinking has led Morgan right back to the arguments typical of all eugenicists and genetic engineers who dream of improving the human race (read: their own class or dominant nation) through selective breeding, immigration quotas and ultimately genocides, only this time the vision of the future is one of women selecting for more amenable men. Again, Morgan, no thanks.

In sum, Morgan's *The Descent of Woman*, which was obviously intended to help demolish androcentric myths about early human evolution which contribute to the oppression of women, ends up attempting to pass off as scientific fact a tremendous number of misconceptions about the workings of genetically grounded evolutionary processes. It repeatedly blurs over the distinction between these processes and the processes of cultural evolution—processes which are not subject to the laws of natural selection, but which nevertheless are now, and have long been, the primary distinguishing characteristic of our species. In so doing, Morgan completely misses the boat on understanding what defines the particularity of human evolution and is therefore just as unable to understand the material basis for the emergence and development of various social contradictions, including in particular the oppression of women.

II

In sharp contrast to Morgan's book is Nancy Make-peace Tanner's 1981 work, *On Becoming Human*. Like Morgan, Tanner is clearly motivated by a desire to expose and shake up the false assumptions which permeate the scientific and popular literature concerning the role of females in early human evolution and which, often in contradiction to the available material evidence, have painted a highly distorted picture of the origins of human beings. While her book deals only with the period of the ape-hominid *divergence*, Tanner clearly recognizes that these distortions are loaded with political and ideological implications which contribute to the *continuing* oppression of women.

Unlike Morgan, however, Tanner seems to understand that in order to deal serious blows to long-enshrined icons, one has to thoroughly and rigorously go after the truth. Her book painstakingly excavates beneath the surface of an assortment of myths; it reveals many aspects of prevailing dogmas which have never really been substantiated, separates these off, and carefully digs into what's left. *On Becoming Human* is an extensive and up-to-date review of hundreds of scientific papers and books (which she cites) in a number of different fields, including paleontology, paleoecology, population genetics, molecular biology, primate behavior, and comparative anthropology. Tanner's method consists largely of identifying points of confluence in the various data available and extracting from this a synthetic picture, one which is probably one of the most substantiated reconstructions of early human evolution to date. While the book is unfortunately somewhat marred by a few sections which call to mind the pitfalls of sociobiology (more on this later), it nevertheless constitutes a valuable contribution to an understanding of our origins and should be of use to anyone seeking to deepen the exposure of the origin myths serving to "keep women in their place."

One of the first problems Tanner focuses on is the way most early evolutionary reconstructions have centered almost exclusively on the presumed role and activities of adult males, leaving females and the young almost totally out of the picture in the transition from ape to human. She stresses once again the absurdity of the prevalent notion that erect posture, bipedality, and the freeing of the hands (with the resultant ability to make and use tools and weapons) were selected for in our earliest ancestors so that some of the ancestral tree-dwelling apes could immediately meet the exigencies of the savanna environments by chasing after big game, killing their prey with stones, and thriving on the meat. According to this classical view the males, unhampered by young, would have been the sole innovators of the new hunting activities. They would have shared their food with the females and young, thereby preventing extinction and ensuring the reproduction of new generations of Mighty Hunter males and passive females and young. Tanner brings out evidence from fossil remains and from comparative primate studies which shows that our ancestors were at one time brachiating apes who used their arms to move through trees and whose grasping feet were better adapted to climbing than to walking—it is unlikely that they engaged in much, if any, bipedal locomotion on the ground. At best they could have been expected to occasionally stand semi-erect, engage in some knuckle-walking on the ground, perhaps sometimes freeing one, or even both, hands for balancing or carrying, but only for very brief periods of time (as happens with our closest living ape relatives today).

That populations of such animals could have begun to move onto the savannas is not at all unexpected. The ancestral ape population itself, though clearly primarily forest inhabitants, may well have been able to exploit a mixture of relatively closed and open forest environments; the fossil records suggest that the apes of this period had the dentition of generalized herbivores, meaning that they subsisted primarily on an assortment of leaves and fruits. They may well have found some of their most palatable meals in forest openings and canopy breaks, along forest edges, rivers, and other marginal environments. While Tanner herself does not explicitly suggest this, it is known that generalized herbivory (i.e., the eating of a broad range of plant materials) in many living tropical species is often correlated with an exploitation of relatively open environments where fast-growing, relatively nontoxic plant materials are usually the most abundant. Add to that the fact, documented by Tanner, that the savannas where many early hominid fossils have been found were not the undifferentiated expanses of open and torrid wastelands that Morgan imagines, but were, like savannas today, variegated environments made up of grasslands interspersed by clumps of trees and broken up by river and lake systems bordered by strips of forest (gallery forests), and the presumed move of some of the ancestral apes into these savannas is not too hard to imagine.

The precise reasons for the move will probably never be explained, but it seems to have taken place in a time of frequent and dramatic climatic and topographical changes marked by volcanic upheavals, the creation of geological rifts and extensive lake and river systems, an overall drying trend, etc. Some of the pioneer populations of the ancestral apes may have been driven onto the savannas by increased competition and shrinking resources; alternatively, the extension of savannas, woodlands, and riverine forest belts may have simply provided some new opportunities for expansion and resource utilization, as well as the basis for reproductive isolation from the ancestral stock. In any case, the switch away from the forests may well have been at first only a switch in emphasis: from occupying primarily closed forest habitats (with some use of open areas) to exploiting primarily open areas, while probably still retreating to clumps of trees and forest strips and edges for shelter from heat and predators and for supplemental foods.

But no matter how much genetic variation these pioneer populations may have exhibited, it is highly unlikely that a whole new species originated on the basis of the sudden appearance of individuals able to stand erect, run across the savannas on two legs, and brandish and throw stones with sufficient power and accuracy to kill big mammals. It is also unlikely that these pioneers could have switched to a diet consisting primarily of meat (in fact, dental remains of the early hominids clearly go against this notion), and there is no reason to think that the males would have shared significant amounts of food with females and the young. What is most likely to have happened, based on the fossil evidence and on studies of our closest living relatives, the African apes, is that, among the populations of ancestral apes who spread onto the savannas, some were able to subsist, reproduce, and get firmly established there because they already had some physiological and behavioral *basis* to make use of the resources present: the savanna plant foods, including a variety of stems, bulbs, tubers, etc., leaves and fruits from scattered patches of trees dotting the landscape, supplemented by insect grubs, termites, occasional bird and reptile eggs, and even more occasional small animals which could be caught with the hands.

This view of the probable diet of the transitional forms is supported not only by the dietary habits of our closest living ape relatives but also by the hominid fossil dental remains which indicate heavy reliance on plant foods; it is further reinforced by the fact that, in the absence of developed productive forces, modern-day human beings are often organized in foraging societies of gatherer-hunters who subsist almost exclusively on a diet of gathered plant foods such as roots, tubers, fruits, nuts, etc., with the addition of grubs, termites, snails, grasshoppers, honey, eggs, etc., as well as occasional lizards, small rodents, or other small animals which can be easily caught by hand. Sometimes the opportunity presents itself to butcher a large animal which has been found dead or which has become stuck in river or lake mud, for instance. But even these gatherer-hunter peoples, who have all the physical and mental attributes which characterize our modern-day species, who use relatively sophisticated weapons such as bows and arrows, assorted blades, traps, plant toxins, etc., and who have means of cooking and processing meat to render it more digestible, still rely only very *secondarily* on hunting for their food supply.[15] This is largely

---

[15]This pattern holds true for the vast majority of basic foraging societies, especially in the tropical or subtropical zones where plant food can be gathered readily throughout the year. In colder zones where the availability of plant foods may be greatly reduced

because hunting is a much more unpredictable activity than gathering: the hunted species are mobile, often scarce, dispersed, and difficult to catch and kill if found. This holds true for most birds, monkeys, and any number of relatively small and harmless prey and even more so for the big, fleet-footed grazing mammals of the savannas and the various potential prey capable of defending themselves. Consider then the absurdity of our common vision of the earliest transitional hominids, recently emerged from a primarily quadrupedal, herbivorous state, suddenly subsisting off the kill of large savanna mammals! The species of mammals most likely encountered by our clumsily lumbering ancestors (who were probably barely able to throw a few sticks) would also either have been too fleet of foot to get caught or too likely to turn our ancestors into a meal (in fact some of the earliest hominid fossils found do seem to be the remains of leopards' dinners).

Everything thus points to the view that the earliest transitional forms diverging from the apes would have

---

during parts of the year, hunting appears to assume correspondingly greater importance. This was the case, for instance, for some of the North American Indian tribes, although here, too, ethnographers and popular reconstructions have traditionally one-sidedly emphasized the importance of hunting and downplayed the importance of gathering (of plant foods, shellfish, etc.) in the procurement of the main food supplies. In addition, many of the North American Indian tribes had more advanced economic bases than true foragers, having developed means of *storing* surplus foods (such as grain, dried or salted fish, etc.). In the more southern regions, tribes depended more on plant foods than on hunting for basic subsistence, and some had advanced horticultural systems (such as the Southwest Pueblos). Even tribes in the colder regions, who depended more on hunting for their food supplies, frequently had seasonal garden plots, usually tended by the women. The Iroquois, for instance, who are commonly depicted only as hunters or fierce warriors, cultivated garden plots and had a correspondingly more complex and stratified social system than that typical of simple foraging societies.

continued to rely mainly on plant foods, supplemented by insects, etc. But the natural distribution of food sources in the new savanna environments would have presented important new difficulties: in their old forest habitats, the fruits, leaves, etc., would have been fairly abundant and relatively evenly distributed. Subsistence could have been insured, as in the living African apes, by foraging over relatively limited distances, usually under a protective tree cover. They could have consumed all the food that was needed, *on the spot*, as they foraged. Under such conditions, social organization could be very loosely structured, perhaps quite similar to that of present-day forest chimpanzees who move through forests in small groups of fluctuating composition devoid of strict hierarchies. Sharing of food would probably be extremely rare, save between a mother and her dependent young, as each adult could easily meet its own nutritional needs; again, as with our closest living relatives, it is conceivable that there was some degree of tool use and even primitive tool modification, as in the stripping of leaves from branches and the use of the resultant sticks for systematic probing and scooping out of insect nests, to knock down fruit, etc. (behaviors commonly exhibited by chimpanzees). But the ancestral apes could have been quite able to survive and reproduce without any further tool use or food hoarding given relatively abundant, reliable, and predictable food supplies.

The savannas were a different story. While much more diverse and teeming with life than many people realize, these ancient savannas, like savannas today, would nevertheless have presented a much more patchy, discontinuous, scattered distribution of food sources to these primarily herbivorous pioneer populations. The patchiness would be both temporal and spatial: temporal, because more clearcut seasonal differences would mean that the availability of many fruits, nuts, etc., would fluctuate more dramatically than in the more closed forest; and spatial, because fairly great distances of open grasslands would separate clumps of trees or narrow strips of riverine forests from which the transitional forms would likely seek the bulk of their food. Eating was no longer just a question of moving a bit further through the trees. Foraging would take more time and be more unpredictable. Those individuals who did not exhibit sufficient behavioral plasticity to adapt to these new conditions would most likely retreat to the forests or simply die out. But among these early pioneer populations there must have been some individuals exhibiting the needed plasticity in such a way as to survive, reproduce, and remain consistently in the new environment, even to the point of becoming reproductively isolated from the ancestral ape populations. This would be the beginning of the speciation process which would eventually lead to modern human beings.

What did this plasticity consist of? Certainly not of an increased brain capacity. Despite the fact that generations of post-Darwinian scientists hoped against all hope to discover that the key feature ensuring the divergence from the apes had been the emergence of a large and complex brain, the fossil record has by now dashed their fondest dreams: it is now incontestably clear that fully erect posture (and the attendant freeing of the hands) evolved *before* any notable expansion of the brain (*see Appendix*).

As pointed out previously, it is reasonable to assume that the ancestral ape population which gave rise to chimpanzees, gorillas, and ourselves may well have been capable of an occasional bit of walking on two or three legs, even if brachiating through trees was the more common form of locomotion. But in this bit of walking lay the basis for the occasional freeing of one or two hands, which were already fairly adept at clasping and which could therefore potentially be used for *carrying*. This, Tanner suggests, must have been the basis for what she considers to be the most critical development in the transition from ape to hominid: *the innovation of gathering*. In support of this, Tanner pieces together evidence from a number of areas: the fossil record, which shows that the early hominids had the dentition of plant-eaters and underwent the key skeletal changes to more fully erect posture; reconstructions of the external environments in which these transitional forms existed, which reveal the patchy, discontinuous nature of the habitats they exploited; the morphological and behavioral characteristics of the living African apes which diverged from the same ape ancestors (and especially the characteristics of the chimpanzees to which we are most closely related), which provide clues as to the pre-existing biological bases which could have served as a substrate for the divergence of the hominid line; and finally, diets, methods of food acquisition, and general lifeways of present-day human beings whose gatherer-hunter societies have subsisted in marginal environments for thousands of years without extensive agriculture or animal domestication, which provide clues as to what may well have been the earliest form of social organization of human beings.[16] All this informa-

---

[16]The gathering-hunting !Kung San peoples of the Dobe area in the African Kalahari Desert, for instance, occupy an area which has been inhabited continuously by gatherer-hunter peoples for more than 11,000 years. Anthropologist Marjorie G. Shostak, who has studied !Kung societies, writes that "gathering and hunting as a way of life has now almost disappeared, but it was the way people lived for nearly 90 percent of the estimated one hundred thousand years of human existence. Adding to this the evolutionary history of our prehuman ancestors would give a period of nearly three million years and a figure closer to 99 percent. Thus this form of human society has been a much more universal human experience than agriculture, which has been practiced for only about ten thousand years, or industrial manufacture, which has existed for only about two hundred years" (Shostak 1981, p. 4)

This author does not, however, share Shostak's view that a basic

tion adds up to suggest that the first great qualitative leap away from the ancestral apes occurred when, in the face of the new necessities imposed by scattered food sources, those individuals best able to survive and reproduce were those who were most able to stand and walk on their hind legs. Why? Not so much because this enabled them to better scan the horizon for possible distant food sources and to detect predators (although this may have played some role), but because the more their hands were freed, the better they could probe, dig out, scoop, and break open whatever food was found, as well as carry it to other places. With the innovation of carry-

---

"human personality" was forged during the millennia when the gathering-hunting ways predominated, a view common among sociobiologists. This view severs human beings' ways of viewing things from the productive and other social relations of particular societies in their motion and development and, further, suggests that current social problems reflect maladaptations of this supposed primeval personality to today's world. And it should also be said that those first three million years or so could not possibly have been a single undifferentiated and completely static period as far as hominid or human social relations are concerned, and must have encompassed important quantitative and qualitative changes and even social upheavals of sorts (for an entertaining and not altogether implausible speculation in novel form of the possible activities and social interactions of Cro-Magnons and Neandertals circa 50,000 years ago, including a failed attempt at animal domestication and the introduction of classes, cf. Björn Kurtén's *Dance of the Tiger*).

Nevertheless, the figures cited by Shostak serve to underscore two points: socially stratified and class-based societies based on the subjugation of whole sections of humanity are comparatively *recent* phenomena and certainly not an immutable part of human social life; and major social change has become telescoped and has been occurring at a tremendously accelerated pace in the course of human history in accordance with accelerating leaps in the productive bases of human societies. While human social relations were surely never completely static, the most frequent and dramatic economic and social upheavals and transformations have been concentrated in only the last few hundred years, and there is every reason to suggest that this has provided a basis for further and even more sweeping social changes on a world scale in the relatively near future.

ing, no longer did the individual have to eat all it could on the spot and then move on, its next meal highly unpredictable in this patchwork environment. It could now carry roots and other foods off the grasslands, perhaps to the shelter of a tree clump for safer consumption, or stash them for later use or simply carry it across a greater expanse of land as it searched for still more food at distant intervals.

Tanner believes that the adult females of these pioneer populations would have been the key innovators of such gathering activities, since bearing and nursing young would place the females under even greater nutritional stresses than the males in these food-scarce environments. Further, it is highly improbable that the social structures of the ancestral primates would have been such that the pioneer males and/or females unencumbered with young would have initially engaged in any significant sharing of plant foods with mothers and their young.[17]

In the mosaic environments into which the pioneer populations seem to have spread, there would appear to have been both an urgent necessity and an at least embryonic morphological and behavioral basis for the emergence of a true gathering innovation; it is not implausible that, as Tanner suggests, this basis existed particularly in the adult *females* who had dependent young. Gathered food would most likely be shared with these infants, and any remaining excess might well fall to older, but not fully mature, young (who often travel with mothers in primate species); these would be likely to engage in some gathering behavior themselves, whether

---

[17]The only ongoing, systematic sharing of plant foods in chimpanzees, for instance, occurs between mothers and their dependent young. Sharing among adults is extremely uncommon, except in relation to the one type of occasionally consumed food which *is* rare and difficult to obtain: meat.

because of an inherited genetic basis, or simply through learning. In fact, regardless of whether it can reasonably be assumed that the females with young were quite possibly the initial innovators in this domain, one would expect the innovation to have spread *rapidly* throughout the transitional populations: the capacity to gather food in excess of immediate needs, and further, to share it with the young—whether directly genetically programmed or resulting from a genetic basis already allowing a fair amount of behavioral plasticity, leading to rapid adjustments to new situations on the basis of learning (a capacity evidenced to varying degrees by all living apes)—would have conferred an immediate, and dramatic, reproductive advantage to those individuals capable of the new behavior. One slight criticism of Tanner's presentation of this question is that she seems to underestimate how rapid this spread would probably be, as individuals of both sexes in a higher primate species would be likely to pick up very quickly on such a new behavior.

While it is, of course, not possible to ascertain absolutely whether the gathering innovation was key in the transition away from the apes—and whether females were the pioneering elements—this reconstruction has the distinct advantage, relative to the more classical models which one-sidedly emphasize hunting, of corresponding much more closely to all the indirect bits and pieces of evidence taken together, from which the basis and likelihood of an early gathering innovation, and its crucial implications, emerge. There was no preordained guarantee that evolution would take a course leading to the emergence of bipedality and of the capacity to gather food in excess of on-the-spot individual consumption. But there is no doubt that it did, and if it hadn't, we simply wouldn't be here to ponder its significance.

As for the possible social structures of our earliest ancestors it is important to remember that the best we can do is to generate informed guesses, based on circumstantial evidence. Whereas fossilized dental and skeletal remains can give us important direct indications of diet, posture, musculature, and mode of locomotion, and whereas the location of the remains can give us a fairly good idea of the environments inhabited, other species encountered, etc., there is no direct evidence for piecing together behavior, and especially social behavior, from the fossil record. For this reason many people have concentrated their attention on our living primate relatives, hoping to discover in their habits and social structures some clues as to our origins. This is not without value, especially if you consider that the current best estimates available suggest that the hominid line diverged from the ancestral ape line (which also gave rise to gorillas and chimpanzees) as recently as 3 to 5 million years ago, instead of 10 million or more as previously thought. As pointed out earlier, this divergence date correlates well with both the fossil record and the new methods of estimating divergence times from biochemical comparisons in related species, which have notably revealed a 99 percent similarity in typical protein chains of chimpanzees and humans. Studies of ape ecology, evolutionary biology, and behavior are therefore not irrelevant for understanding some things about early human evolution, as long as the obvious limitations are recognized, including in particular the fact that the gorilla and chimpanzee species are themselves a product of divergence from the ancestral line, which signifies that we can only speculate about what features they shared with our common ape ancestor; the fact that *all* the higher primates rely to a great extent on *learning* in their social relations (even for such basics as mating and maternal care of young, for instance); and finally, and most crucially, that while all the higher primates exhibit an impressive capacity to learn, the divergence leading to human beings has represented a qualitative leap in this ability, to the point where cultural evolution has come to far outstrip processes of biological evolution in mediating change in the human species. In fact the very figures on the close biochemical relatedness of humans and chimpanzees should serve to underscore that fact: on the one hand, the two species are apparently extremely close at the level of the organization of the basic building blocks of protein chains—yet, on the other hand, our capacity for self-consciousness, our ability to transform our environments, our recording of history and visions of the future, our complex social relations, all point to a qualitative difference which can only be explained in terms of factors and processes not under rigid and slow-changing genetic programming.

Unfortunately, the scientific and popular literature frequently blurs over this distinction and is therefore cluttered with innumerable unfounded extrapolations from the behavior of other primates to those of human beings. Studies of higher primates have, among other things, enabled us to understand that we are biologically quite closely related to some other species, that some aspects of behaviors once thought to be exclusively human are not restricted to our species (such as some aspects of sexuality), and that all the higher primates rely to a fair extent on learning, suggesting that much of *their* social behaviors may not be under direct genetic control. But this very fact, combined with the qualitatively *greater* degree to which the human species exhibits a capacity for learning and unprecedented behavioral flexibility, is exactly why direct extrapolations from the social systems and behaviors of other primates to those of the fully human *Homo sapiens* species are quite frankly useless, or worse.[18]

---

[18]Sarah Blaffer Hrdy's book *The Woman That Never Evolved*, for instance, presents much interesting and provocative information on such things as the role of females in determining social structures in various primate species, the tremendous variety of primate social

Tanner is not unaware of the limitations inherent in comparative primate studies and the attempts to draw direct extrapolations from other primates to modern human beings. But because she is dealing primarily with the process of *becoming* human (the title she has given her book), thus focusing almost exclusively on attempting to reconstruct the *transition* from the ancestral apes to the earliest hominids, the fact that she delves extensively into the literature on chimpanzees and other close relatives of humans is much more justified. Her intent is to dispel many of the Tarzanist myths of early human evolution and attempt a more scientific reconstruction of the transition, and to show how biological processes of selection and speciation could have led to the emergence of a new species whose change and development would thereafter be mediated mainly by cultural processes.

Chimpanzees, in Tanner's view, probably represent the closest thing we can get to a model of the ancestral apes from which both humans and chimpanzees diverged in the relatively recent past. She believes that the

---

structures (some male-centered, some female-centered, etc.), patterns of female sexuality in the higher primates, and distinctions between the higher primates and other mammals in the degree to which the males provide any care for the young. From another angle, Hrdy's book also contains some valuable information and some thought-provoking notions about various means through which the subjugation of females has been accomplished in human societies, including through forcible restrictions of female sexuality to control their reproduction and lines of descent (more on this later). Unfortunately this book suffers from typical sociobiological problems: not only the tendency to treat everything as adaptations having evolved to maximize reproductive potentials, but also the tendency to continually blur over the essential *distinctions* between human social structures and those of all other primates. Thus, while she has some notion that the oppression of women is connected to such things as the division of labor and property relations, Hrdy is unable to bring out why this might be, other than to fall back into biodeterminist theories and focus narrowly on the workings of natural selection.

information available on this species can help give us an idea of what might have been the "bases for the evolution of the capacity for culture" (p. 116). Tanner's case for her choice of chimpanzees as the species best suited for a reconstruction of the ancestral ape line is fairly convincing: indeed chimpanzees exhibit many features of anatomy and habitat which were almost certainly common to our ape ancestors—they are primarily a forest-dwelling species, although capable of exploiting a range of habitats (including savanna woodlands); they eat primarily leaves and fruit but supplement this diet with insects and, very occasionally, meat; they brachiate through the trees but are capable of semi-erect posture and locomotion on the ground and even of a fair degree of tool use in food acquisition, as well as limited carrying. The only other living primate which also diverged from the same ancestral line as humans and chimps is the gorilla, which seems to be a more specialized species, more restricted anatomically and behaviorally, and apparently keyed in more specifically to deep-forest habitats. Gorillas also exhibit a great deal of sexual dimorphism and more rigid social hierarchies. A further indication that chimpanzees are probably closer to the ancestral population is that the two broad groupings of chimpanzees—the common chimpanzees and the pygmy chimpanzees—have remained extremely similar to each other, despite the fact that they presumably became two distinct groups nearly 3 million years ago. This suggests a fairly "conservative lineage," and one which is therefore likely to have preserved many features of the ancestral species.

Finally, in addition to their broad dietary range and broad range of habitats, chimpanzees are perhaps foremost among the apes in exhibiting a broad behavioral plasticity and capacity for learning, including the ability to learn relatively complex modes of communication. Some individual chimps have even learned to communicate with humans in limited fashion through the use of deaf-mute sign language and computer-generated abstract signal systems, which they could never have encountered in the course of their biological evolution, and some recent studies suggest that they are even capable of teaching such acquired signals to young untutored chimps without human mediation. The combination of all these factors suggests that chimps probably are "the closest we can get" to an idea of our direct ape ancestors, keeping in mind the limitations discussed above.

Surprisingly enough, this view is nothing short of heresy among many who attempt reconstructions of early human evolution or who are interested in the possible roots of human social behavior. This is likely because chimps don't do much for the Tarzan and Jane models: they commonly have relatively loose social structures, fluid bands whose size fluctuates frequently depending on food availability; the one consistently identifiable social unit is that of an adult female traveling with dependent young and older offspring and sharing food with them; the females commonly mate with many males, and often initiate copulation; and the males exhibit very few clear dominance relations among themselves, and little or no such behavior towards the females. And such a loose life style might have been that of our ape ancestors? Tsk, tsk, where have all the morals gone? Isn't it common knowledge that male superiority and dominance over females is part of our earliest biological heritage? Or is it? But fear not, there's always the trusty baboon!

Savanna baboons, as Tanner correctly points out, have been the favored primate when it comes to extrapolating about early hominid (and modern human) social behavior. You see, these baboons live on the African savannas and, more to the point, they have extremely rigid social hierarchies, are often spectacularly aggressive and territorial, and organize themselves into bands which are run with an iron fist by one or a few very big macho males (referred to as alpha-males). The younger males and the small and relatively defenseless females seem to cower before these "alphas" in the most abject submission, while these big males strut their stuff, protect the bands from predators, and procure meat. Now surely here's a species we can identify with—at least according to assorted behaviorists and sociobiologists. Implicitly or explicitly, savanna baboons have been repeatedly proposed as models for our own earliest origins or as a basis for understanding human aggression, xenophobia, class structure, and the domination of women, all seen as rooted in biological evolution (and by implication, thus very resistant to change). Even assuming for the moment that such things *were* grounded in our biological evolution in such *direct* fashion (which they most certainly are not), there would still be a huge problem with selecting baboons as the best source of clues concerning human social behavior: they aren't even closely related to us. In fact they are not even apes, but *monkeys*, a whole different evolutionary line, and one which is qualitatively more distant from us than the gorillas and chimpanzees with which we at least share a common ancestor. Given this, and even though savanna baboons constitute an interesting species in its own right, it is truly amazing that their social behavior could have been used so blatantly as a reference point for human behavior. The fact that savanna baboons have to deal with conditions which are probably close to what the early hominids encountered says nothing about how these conditions were "responded to" in an evolutionary sense. Given a different morphological, behavioral, and ecological *historical* basis, the two lines would likely have evolved along quite different routes. For instance, baboons and patas monkeys both live in very similar environments and deal with similar predator pressures, but baboons form large troops of males and females traveling together with a "male protective unit," while patas monkeys have no such protective unit and rely on hiding and silence to evade predators, or rapid noisy scattering if discovered. Thus a similar environment can correlate with many different morphological and behavioral features and, aside from random events, which features evolve is largely conditioned by the *prior* material bases available, the inherited forms and developmental pathways which channel and restrict evolutionary change (Gould and Lewontin 1979, p. 594). As Tanner correctly emphasizes: "A species' ecological adaptation and social organization are related not only to features of the environment—such as food availability and location or predator pressures—but also to the evolutionary history of the species itself" (p. 21). In this respect Tanner's book plays an important role in puncturing the sociobiology types' favorite primate model.

Some might ask, even if a chimpanzee-style model of generalized herbivore with loose, fluid, female-centered social units more plausibly corresponds to the ancestral populations which expanded onto the savannas, why couldn't they nevertheless have evolved into a more baboon-like species, complete with heavy male dominance, aggression, etc.? This is not absolutely impossible theoretically, but it is very unlikely given not only the probable characteristics of the ancestral apes (inferred from the "conservative lineage" represented by our chimpanzee relatives) but also a number of trends which we *know* took place. We know the early hominids evolved erect posture, full bipedality and attendant freeing of the hands; this would have provided a basis for gathering, which is probably the most basic of all human "productive" activities, and would also have provided a basis for dealing with predators—while trees could still provide some shelter, a basis existed for chasing predators away by thrashing the arms and throwing sticks and stones at them long before weapons were invented, much as has been observed in chimps attempting to repel live predators or even the stuffed model of a leopard. And as pointed out earlier, the trend in the hominid line has not been towards increased sexual dimorphism and larger canine "fighting teeth" (all of which are characteristic of savanna baboons and would be expected to occur in a primate species with strict social hierarchies, having one dominant sex, relying on aggressive encounters for defense, etc.). In fact, as noted earlier, just the opposite trend seems to have occurred: a reduction in the size of the canine teeth (and quite likely in the dimorphism between males and females) even before the appearance of weapons which could have substituted for teeth. (It should also be noted that even the likely increase in predator pressure encountered on the savannas might well have worked against the development of more "aggressive" modes of behavior, strict hierarchies, and dominance by sex in the early hominids. An increase in predator pressure could possibly reduce the amount of competition among the transitional forms themselves relative to the level of competition among their forest-dwelling forebears. In a wide variety of species of plants and animals, reduced competition for resources among individuals of a given species has been tentatively correlated with increases in predator pressure as the predators serve to "thin out" the populations they prey on.)

Surely all these facts bode ill for all those who like to picture our earliest ancestors as constantly fighting males accompanied by weak and docile females! The more plausible scenario is that there was, at first, little basis for dominance by either sex, and reliance more on evasion than direct confrontation for dealing with predators (not always successfully). But this is where we have to start examining the full social repercussions of the gathering innovation as it spread throughout a population.

Assuming the most plausible argument—that the transitional forms originally brought with them the relatively fluid social structures of a chimp-like generalized herbivore centered around basic units formed by females and their young of varied ages and correspondingly varied degrees of association—one of the first social consequences of gathering (aside from the increased survival and reproduction of the innovators) would be that it would provide a basis for increased social cohesion and the formation of larger groups. Gathered food in excess of whatever was consumed on the spot would likely be *shared* beyond the immediate mother-infant unit, first with older young, and finally with other adult individuals not necessarily closely related. These individuals, who tended to congregate in larger bands and to allow excess food to be consumed more broadly, would probably be better protected from predators and better assured of a regular food supply than those who continued to forage on their own, or who limited their sharing to their own young. In the absence of selection mechanisms pulling strongly in an opposite direction, groups would thus probably tend to become larger, though they might remain extremely loose for some time. Tanner suggests that with the emergence of the gathering innovation, quite possibly spearheaded by females under the greatest nutritional stress, the key factor in the divergence from the apes had materialized. (Tanner also reports that chimpanzee females who share food with young apparently use tools in such activities as insect collecting for more extended periods of time than males.) The best gatherers would have been those best able to walk erect and to use crude tools for collecting and carrying. These individuals and their young would be more likely to survive.

This prompts Tanner to say that "the intelligence to gather (i.e., to learn, improve upon, and teach this crucial innovation) and the sociability to share with off-spring doubtless were enhanced by natural selection just as were anatomical changes related to bipedalism and skilled use of the hands. These changes enhanced the survival of the mothers themselves and of their children" (pp. 268-69). This formulation presents some problems because there is an implication here, found elsewhere throughout the book, that such concepts as "intelligence," "sociability," "disruptiveness," and even the "gathering innovation" itself can be treated as discrete, actually existing entities (a fallacy known as reification), and that these entities are directly the result of genetic programming. But there is no basis to suggest this, and it is highly unlikely: in fact in modern humans there is no evidence whatsoever for direct genetic programming of specific social behaviors. Tanner quotes evolutionary biologist Ernst Mayr to bring out the fact that a specific behavioral innovation can often be "the most important evolutionary determinant, particularly in the initiation of new evolutionary trends" (p. 160), which is demonstrably true, but she does not sufficiently recognize the fact that "the greater the developmental flexibility of the phenotype, the better a species can cope with a selection pressure *without* genetic reconstruction" (Mayr 1983, p. 331, emphasis added).

There is little doubt that individuals most exhibiting erect posture and able to use their hands to dig out, collect, and carry food would have had a tremendous reproductive advantage in savanna environments, and that natural selection would have favored these phenotypes by ensuring their spread. But whether this new behavior was specifically genetically encoded or simply an expression of a genetic basis allowing for a broad degree of behavioral plasticity—as for instance, an increased capacity to learn—would have had very different implications. In both cases natural selection would favor the "result," so to speak, but in the second case one would expect the particular innovation to spread more rapidly and more broadly throughout the population (through learning) than if it was more *specifically* genetically programmed. While it might still be true that females had been the initial innovators of the new behavior (because in the face of greater nutritional stress those exhibiting the greatest behavioral plasticity had best been able to survive and reproduce), the "gathering innovation" *per se* would in this case simply be a particular expression of a general plasticity likely to be present in both sexes; and if learning was already a key aspect of this plasticity, the innovation would not long remain the province of the females, a fact which Tanner seems to alternately underestimate or attribute to different causes (in particular female choice of mates—more on this later).

While it is most likely true that "transitional hominid fathers. . . would not know their young" (Tanner, p. 161), whereas female behavior could more directly affect the survival of their dependent young, there is no reason to postulate that natural selection would have operated that much more intensely on the females, or that there would have been much lag time in the males acquiring this new behavior—especially if the new behavior was one manifestation of the evolution of genetic complexes coding for a *wide range* of behaviors. Such plasticity would clearly be advantageous to both sexes in the new and more unpredictable environment. Here Tanner falls into something of an eclectic muddle. She states that "for males it was primarily their individual survival that was at issue in terms of natural selection" (p. 162). But even if the males were not directly involved in the care of the young[19] and the

---

[19]While ancestral transitional males are certainly unlikely to have contributed directly to the care of the young to any great extent, it should be pointed out that the living higher primates are unusual

females were therefore more able to directly influence the survival and reproduction of their offspring, males capable of full bipedality and food-gathering behaviors would themselves have had better chances of surviving longer periods in the new environments and therefore of producing more young. Thus even if the manifestation of the new behavior in any given male did not contribute as directly and dramatically to reproductive success as that same behavior manifested by an individual female involved in the long-term care of the young, there is no basis for Tanner's categorical statement that the males' "plant foraging efficacy would not appear to affect their reproductive success" (p. 162). Further, all males are, after all, their mothers' sons! Regardless of the degree or lack of specificity of genetic programming involved, the sons of the "innovators" would likely manifest the same abilities, either through inheritance of specific programs, or through the kind of learning which is common among all higher primates. All of this suggests that there is little reason to invoke any significant ongoing sexual segregation of these capacities.

Along the same lines, Tanner gets into trouble on the questions of the particular manifestations of the natural selection process known as kin selection and sexual selection. Kin selection is the expression commonly used to describe a hypothetical process particularly dear to the heart of many sociobiologists. In this model, natural selection may favor certain characteristics and behaviors of individuals which reduce or even preclude their own *direct* individual reproduction—*if* these characteristics or behaviors favor the survival and reproduction of other individuals who are closely *related*

---

among mammals in the degree to which the males indirectly (and sometimes directly) care for the young (Hrdy1981, p. 72). This leaves open the possibility that care of the young was perhaps not exclusively engaged in by females even in the ancestral species.

and who therefore presumably have many genes in common with the so-called "altruistic" individual. The idea is that by contributing to the survival and reproduction of its close relatives, even at the expense of its own direct reproduction, an individual could conceivably spread its own genes even more than if it did so only through its direct offspring. In its simplest form this concept, despite the anthropomorphism of the term "altruism," is not necessarily opposed to the basic, and unconscious, workings of natural selection at the level of individual organisms; it provides a likely explanation, for instance, for much of the seemingly "altruistic" phenomena in the social insects. The problem with kin selection is that this concept has been much abused, being applied indiscriminately (especially by sociobiologists) to explain a wide variety of behaviors in social species with little or no consideration of alternative hypotheses.

Most harmfully, kin selection has in recent years been invoked to repeatedly suggest that many human social behaviors and phenomena are rooted in (usually unconscious) biologically determined reproductive strategies designed to optimize the transmission of an individual's genes to future generations, rather than arising from nonbiological material origins. All sociobiological theories as applied to human beings have in common one thing: a blatant disregard for the fact that specific social behaviors in humans are not known to be tied to specific inheritable genetic bases—and are clearly more determined by acquired cultural considerations than by any genetic reconstructions mediated by natural selection. And there is a further methodological problem in these sociobiological theories because, in any case, human social relations and institutions are precisely social and not simply collections of acts and behaviors of individuals.

As Lewontin has perceptively noted:

The basic philosophical error is the confusion of properties of sets with properties of members of sets. The basic methodological problem is that beginning with a biological determinism of the behavior of individuals as primary and social behavior as consequential on individual behavior, it is simply impossible to deal with uniquely social properties. There is no way, for example, that sociobiological theory can deal with human social institutions that might be universal despite genetic variation within the population, or social changes that occur on a time scale much more rapid than population genetic changes, or with social institutions that may remain constant despite genetic change. That is because sociobiology sees human institutions as the direct consequence of human genotypes and therefore cannot deal with the dynamics of social properties that are not dynamically linked to genetic changes. (Lewontin 1979, p. 9)

Tanner treads gingerly around the issue of kin selection and related topics, avoiding the heart of the controversy surrounding sociobiology. She is clearly no fan of some of the crudest forms of sociobiological determinism (she decries theories of the "selfish gene," for instance), but her rupture with the sociobiological influence is incomplete.

One might excuse Tanner on the grounds that she is dealing with the period of the *transition* away from the apes, a time when culture *per se* had not yet emerged and when change mediated by cultural factors would not yet have outstripped and superceded change mediated by biological evolutionary processes. But she *is* dealing with the period of the emergence of the basis for this switch; the emergence of bipedality (perhaps in conjunction with a trend to neoteny), with everything that entailed in terms of free use of hands, gathering abilities, etc., *itself* provided the basis for variable and flexible interactions in a *variety* of external circumstances, and set the stage for the increased reliance on learning and the active transformation of the outside world which would increasingly characterize the hominid line. Yet Tanner suggests that in the early transition, kin selection would likely have played an important role because, in units of closely related females and young, all the individuals concerned would increase the spread of their genes if they shared food and cared for each other since they had many genes in common relative to the population as a whole; adult males who occasionally helped out, shared food, etc., would also spread more genes and hence increased sociability would be favored. Here again, implicit and unsubstantiated assumptions are made concerning the specific programming and inheritability of fairly complex social behaviors. If on the other hand, and as is more likely, the developing sociability, communication, and learning exchanges were simply manifestations of genetic complexes coding for *wide ranges* of social behaviors expressed variably in relation to varying circumstances, then natural selection would have rapidly favored such plasticity throughout the populations as a whole without necessarily effecting any major genetic reconstructions; there would then be little reason to invoke kin selection at the level of female-centered units as a particular impetus of change.

A similar critique applies to Tanner's treatment of sexual selection, an approach which frankly seems to stem from a subjective pull toward attributing a particularly key role to females in the transition from ape to human. Her treatment seems to be a somewhat contrived and unnecessary speculation with little substantiated basis, detracting somewhat from the main body of her powerful and refreshing exposition on the central role played by gathering in human evolution. Sexual selection is a phenomenon first described by Darwin and best interpreted as a component part of the process of natural selection rather than as a clearly distinct process. It refers to the observable phenomena whereby individuals of either sex gain reproductive advantage through characteristics which make them in some sense more "attractive" to the opposite sex or better able to repel others of the same sex (thereby enhancing their own mating frequency and success) or, conversely, through features which make one sex exercise fine discrimination in its choice of mates of the opposite sex. The features selected for via sexual selection can include such things as the bright showy coloration of a male peacock's tail or a different eye pigment in a fruit fly. The features themselves are not necessarily more broadly adaptive, although they may reflect or be linked to features which do have more direct adaptive value; often, especially in cases where one sex seems to carefully discriminate in its choice of mates, the particular characteristics seem to be features which "stand out" simply because they are *rare* in a population (for instance in a laboratory fruit fly population the females may mate preferentially with the rare males who exhibit a mutation leading to a new eye coloration). Significantly, sexual selection has often been discussed when it seems to involve competition between males for females, which does in fact occur in many species, but the related and also prevalent phenomenon of female choice of mates has often been ignored—perhaps because the very notion has some disturbing ideological connotations for humans of chauvinist persuasion! In cases where sexual discrimination of mates is apparent, the sex which does the discriminating often seems to be the sex which exhibits the greater degree of what has been termed "parental investment" (a term referring to the degree of energy expenditure in the production of young and in ensuring their viability). In many species, though not all, this sex is the female, and the phenomenon of mate discrimination is therefore commonly referred to as "female choice."

Tanner believes that female choice played a crucial role in the process of divergence of the transitional hominids from the ancestral apes. She reasons that careful female discrimination of mates would have become increasingly important in the more unpredictable savanna environments and, given the trend towards increased dependence of the young, incorporation of more "helpful" adult males into the basic social units (females and young) on a more ongoing basis would have been advantageous in terms of protection and increased food supply.

There is no doubt that in the transition away from the ancestral apes the period of juvenile dependency increased, but Tanner's insistence on the likely importance of female choice of mates seems to rest on a number of shaky assumptions. In particular, she seems to assume that there was a fairly long period of time after the earliest appearance of bipedality and gathering when sufficiently significant behavioral differences continued to exist between the two sexes (assuming that the first innovators of gathering were females). Under such conditions the careful choice of mates by females—picking those who were the most bipedal, inclined to gather and to share food—would enhance their potential for survival and reproduction. In this view female choice would contribute to pushing the evolution of the species in the same direction as natural selection overall, thus reinforcing and speeding up the process of generalizing the new features. But the *basis* underlying the new gathering behavior was the emergence of bipedality (which freed the hands), a change which did require some genetic reconstruction (quite possibly in conjunction with a trend towards retention of juvenile characteristics) and there is no reason to think that this, the emergence of *bipedality*, would have been more restricted to one sex than the other, even if some of the females were the first to translate some of the attendant flexibility into a behavioral innovation—gathering.

In other words, the capacity for systematic tool use and collection of food must have existed wherever bipedality had emerged, and most likely appeared at pretty much the same rate in both sexes. Add to that the fact that even the ancestral apes probably exhibited some capacity for learning by imitation, like all living primates, and it is reasonable to suspect the innovation spread like wildfire among both sexes, even if it continued to be manifested differentially between them (i.e., even if females spent more time gathering than males, for instance). It is true that individual males who added to this basic capacity a tendency to hang around mothers and young and to share food, including that which they themselves had gathered, would likely mate more often and also unconsciously contribute to the increased survival of their own young so that the characteristics of both males and females in these units would be likely to spread to a greater extent than those of individuals maintaining more independent foraging and eating patterns. In this limited sense there may be some basis for suggesting that preferential female choice of the best gatherer-sharer males might further speed up what would anyway have been the extremely rapid spread of those characteristics without which the pioneer populations could probably not have become established in the new marginal environments. But it is not necessary to insist, as does Tanner, that a special increase in discrimination of mates by the females would have been a requirement of full speciation from the ancestral ape populations (cf. Tanner, p. 161).

The emergence of bipedality and related features, which may well have been an absolute prerequisite of establishment on the savannas, would likely have been a sufficiently dramatic and rapidly enough generalized leap to ensure reproductive isolation from the ancestral stock—even if they were to overlap again after a short time. Tanner's insistence on the role of female choice in the hominid speciation process is based on the theory that overlap of the two populations would occur due to insufficient dietary and geographic barriers (which is probably true), and that in such cases repeated inter-breeding, preventing full speciation, would have been avoided only if the females had mated solely with the males who were the most divergent from the ancestral norm—i.e., the most bipedal, etc. While such female choice may have been a factor in the speciation process, it is not, as Tanner suggests, the only process which could have ensured sufficient reproductive isolation for full speciation.

If bipedality, freer use of hands, and attendant changes actually did spread very rapidly in small pioneer populations which had become at least temporarily iso-lated in an environment where "nondivergent" indivi-duals had little chance of survival, one might expect the following: only extremely divergent individuals would be likely to survive in the new environment; the prob-ably already small populations of pioneers might well be even further reduced for some time, thereby reducing the chances of overlap with the ancestral stock through ran-dom movement and providing some chance for temporal isolation; and finally, even if significant overlap did oc-cur relatively soon, the severe morphological and behavioral differences of the most divergent individuals of both sexes could well serve as a barrier to their mating with the ancestral stock. If some of the less divergent ones did mate with the ancestral stock, their offspring would be less likely to become established in the new environments than the offspring of the most divergent individuals among themselves. And if the beginning divergence was marked not only by the emergence of bipedality, but also by a trend towards the retention of juvenile characters (neoteny), the newly divergent individuals would have increasingly looked to both sexes of the ancestral stock like a bunch of odd-postured, sexually immature youngsters—a fact not likely to encourage matings! For a number of reasons, then, it seems that Tanner is a little too quick to put so much emphasis on sexual selection at the hands of the females as an essential driving force in the evolution of humans.

In sum, the weakest part of Tanner's book is the section in which she proposes a sex-linked driving force in the speciation process itself. In particular there seems to be a tendency to assume that complex social behaviors are genetically programmed.[20] In all fairness, Tanner is careful to link complex behaviors to presumed "gene complexes" rather than to single genes, and she periodically stresses that many of the behaviors she is describing are learned. Her comments about culture further suggest that she would not favor strictly biodeterminist theories in relation to modern human beings especially. Yet her thinking in this area is eclectic and contradictory. There are repeated and unfounded assumptions of the inheritability of such things as "intelligence," "friendliness," "disruptiveness," etc., and, again, her suggestion of sexual selection through female choice of mates exhibiting more sociability, food sharing, etc.—whose genes would tend to then spread in the population—is problematical. It looks suspiciously like an assumption that these specific behaviors are clearly

---

[20]Again, this is a common, and politically loaded, assumption promoted by the sociobiologists, despite the fact, pointed out by Stephen Jay Gould among others, that the correct answer to the question "What is the direct evidence for genetic control of specific human social behavior?" is "At the moment. . . none whatever." Gould also stresses that such specific genetic coding is unlikely because the expanded human brain makes possible nonprogrammed learning and because "direct programming of behavior has probably become inadaptive" in the course of the evolution of the human species (Gould 1977, pp. 254, 257; cf. also Gould 1981, pp. 324-34).

delineated entities backed by a specific genetic code rather than, as is more likely, stemming from a genetic makeup permitting a wide range of contradictory behaviors whose particular expression would vary in relation to changing external conditions and therefore could not be tightly specified by the genetic code in any one instance.

It is true that Tanner does say in summation that "Indeed, in a sense, culture *is* the human adaptation" (p. 277), but she does not always consistently follow through on this essential point. It is in fact quite likely that the most significant particularity of human beings relative to other species is the extent to which complex specific behaviors are *not* directly genetically programmed. This has allowed for the tremendous plasticity and behavioral adjustments which have enabled human beings to expand into innumerable environments and to continually transform the external world to a qualitatively greater degree than any other species on earth. If this great plasticity, rooted in our extreme dependence on learning in all that we do, results from a genetic makeup allowing for a great range of contradictory behaviors and is a distinguishing feature of our species, it is very likely to have evolved and been selected for at the time of the first great leap away from the ancestral species—to have been closely linked to the emergence of full bipedality and the resultant freeing of the hands, the capacity for gathering, and other forms of systematic labor. While brain expansion came after the development of bipedality, selection for bipedality— especially if it proceeded through the retention of the juvenile characteristics of the ancestral stock and a slowing down of developmental rates overall—would quickly have provided the basis required for beginning brain expansion and increasing dependence on learning. (Recall that one of the apparent neotenic features in human development is the late closure of the skull sutures, allowing for considerable brain development after birth; other primates are basically born with brains which cannot undergo significant postnatal expansion.)

The embryonic material basis for cultural evolution had emerged. It would eventually greatly supersede the processes of natural selection and biological evolution in mediating change in human societies. Such changes would now occur at a phenomenally greater *rate* than changes mediated by processes of biological evolution, it would *spread* much more broadly and rapidly and would be *modifiable* to a much greater degree and in various directions (Gould 1978, pp. 83-84). Part of Tanner's eclectics seems to reside in a certain underestimation of how *quickly* processes of cultural evolution could supplant processes of genetically restricted biological evolution on the heels of the gathering innovation, which for the first time set the stage for the accumulation of surpluses in human societies, and for the unprecedented capacity to transform the external conditions confronted by the species.

What changes were to follow the emergence of bipedality 3 or 4 million years ago? Most likely, once the major qualitative leap in divergence from the ancestral apes had been accomplished, the early hominids would have continued to evolve more gradually along the lines set by this major rupture to bipedality, routine use of hands and of crude tools in gathering, etc. The ability to gather would provide the basis for a continuing trend in the direction of the retention of juvenile characteristics and retarded development—which was probably at the root of the initial changes. This would lead in turn to individuals who could remain dependent for increasingly long periods of time in a juvenile state. And this would result in a longer period for learning and for the integration of increasingly complex information about the environment and the hominid society itself—but this could only begin to occur when it became possible to care for and feed these more immature individuals for more extended periods of time, i.e., when routine gathering could ensure fairly reliable food supplies. The previously existing communicatory repertoire (which may well have been quite extensive, as it is with chimpanzees today who use numerous gestures, vocalizations, facial expressions, etc., in communicating with each other) could then have been greatly expanded, which would be particularly advantageous to individuals confronted by the patchy resource distributions of savanna environments: selection would favor the ability to remember and communicate the location of food and water sources which were spatially or temporally dispersed. As the ability to process and integrate more complex information evolved, more complex social relations would develop. Groups would expand, generalize, and pass along learned tidbits concerning tool use and modification and would increasingly coordinate their activities, moving in larger groups for more efficient food-gathering and sharing, repulsion of predators, etc. The restricted range of vocalizations of the ancestral apes would not be sufficient to encompass all the new experiences in the new and more unpredictable environments and the increasingly complex social organization. Increased motor coordination which is a prerequisite for more flexible use of the hand would also permit more complex vocalizations. As hands became more efficient for gathering, as gathering increasingly provided the basis for sustaining longer-learning young and led to tighter social organization, selection would probably also favor the capacity for expanded and more flexible repertoires of vocalizations, and the rudiments of human language would emerge.[21]

---

[21]The evolution of the capacity for language has once again traditionally been associated with the emergence of hunting, being needed presumably to coordinate the hunters' efforts. This of course says

Once the full leap to bipedality had occurred and the divergence from the ancestral apes was clearly effected (some 3 or 4 million years ago by best current estimates), the essential biological basis had been laid for all future evolution of the hominid line. Yet even in the earliest times this development was, as all else, uneven, and did not occur along a smooth, unidirectional continuum. The fossil evidence suggests that the early hominids were extremely *variable*, judging from the great variety of jaw and tooth sizes and shapes and related skull features. The earliest known unquestionable hominids (currently usually designated *Australopithecus afarensis*) were bipedal, generally slight of build, and of reduced facial features relative to fossil apes; they have been referred to as "gracile" hominids. They were still relatively small-brained and generally fairly ape-like. Fossils from more recent times are more abundant and are extremely variable, leading to their having been classified into various "species" on a necessarily somewhat arbitrary basis.

Once again, it is important to keep in mind that since all hominid evolution is unlikely to have proceeded on a smooth, gradual continuum and was almost certainly marked by breaks and discontinuities, we should not expect to find unbroken fossil series neatly linked by gradual changes (Gould and Eldredge 1977). But the rough scenario which emerges, as described by Tanner, is that a "gracile" *A. afarensis* form seems to have been followed in time by a still relatively gracile but perhaps

---

nothing of the existing bases for such a development to occur, and is further rendered unlikely by the fact that modern-day humans stalking and hunting game in open environments such as savannas or deserts (as opposed to more closed forests) typically remain extremely quiet. Among the !Kung gatherer-hunters, for instance, the hunters communicate through brief whistles, if at all. Gatherers, on the other hand, regularly shout out to keep track of each other when fanning out over a large area to forage (Shostak 1981).

somewhat more "robust" or heavy-featured form, *A. africanus*; this form then seems to have been succeeded in time by two fairly different types: a very gracile form on the one hand (designated *Australopithecus habilis* or *Homo habilis*) and a very robust form (*A. robustus*). These latter two forms apparently overlapped in time and place and may even have interacted to a certain degree (and perhaps even interbred). Their fossils are associated with the time of appearance of the first crude stone tools which could be used for cutting and scraping. Although more complicated weapons suitable for hunting had not yet emerged, there is evidence from this period of "butchering" activities—the use of crude stone flakes to cut off chunks of flesh from the carcasses of big mammals (which at first were probably simply found dead or trapped in bogs or silt).

A significant feature which emerges from Tanner's review is that the *initial* trend in hominid development after the divergence seems to have been towards increased robusticity, i.e., towards becoming bulkier with more massive jaws and facial musculature and, while canine teeth remained small, towards increasingly big molar teeth. All of this is consistent with a diet consisting predominantly of tough-fibered plant foods characteristic of savannas. The observed subsequent dichotomy in the *Australopithecines* between a very robust and a very gracile form seems to have occurred roughly two million years ago, at a time marked by a dramatic drying trend. The early hominids of this period would presumably have had to rely more than ever on the dry, tough-fibered plant foods of the savanna. Under such conditions, one possible evolutionary route would have been marked by the development of an even more specialized "grinding apparatus" suggested by the massive jaws and huge molars of the robust form. But other evolutionary pathways might have been possible. The absence of this specialized grinding apparatus in the more gracile form and its slight build overall suggest that it must have relied more heavily on *tool use* to break up and process the tough plant foods.[22] What eventually happened to the robust form of this period is not clear: it may have died out altogether, or been subjected to reverse selection pressures away from the big grinding teeth, or have eventually "blended in" with the more gracile forms. The one thing which is clear is that the features of the robust form disappear from the fossil record whereas the more gracile—and presumably more tool-using—form subsists.

This then is a further indication that the successful trends leading to modern humans were those which, very early on, were leading to increased behavioral plasticity and abilities to transform the external world. As Tanner puts it, "Reliance on tools and social tradition are part of our genus's earliest heritage. The social transmission of gathering skills and technology was a critical aspect of the transition from ape-ancestor to early hominid. This increasing importance of social and technological tradition—incipient culture if you will— proceeded together with biological evolution *from the very beginning of the hominid divergence*" (p. 275, emphasis added). And it should be reemphasized that exact-

---

[22]And perhaps to supplement its diet with occasional scavenged meat. Richard Leakey, for one, stresses the fact that our ancestors would likely have been scavengers making use of occasional carcasses long before they had the capacity to engage in any significant hunting. His most recent dates trace the appearance of clear butchering sites (revealing the use of stone implements for cutting and scraping meat off caracasses, though not yet for hunting) at about 1.5 million years ago. He points out that this roughly corresponds to the time our genus ranged out of Africa, becoming firmly established in Asia by one-half million years ago. As a side point, Leakey is also quick to remind us that modern *Homo sapiens* dates back at least 100,000 years and that one should recognize as Eurocentric bias the common tendency to date the appearance of our species from only 40,000 years ago—when it first appeared in Europe!

ly because culturally mediated change occurs much faster, can spread much more broadly, and is eminently more modifiable than changes wrought by biological evolution, it would necessarily have soon far outstripped change based on genetic variation as the motive force in human societies.

What then can be said about the origins of unequal relations in human societies, of the emergence of social hierarchies and of classes, and of the thousands of years of oppression of women by men? While Tanner's book deals only with our earliest origins as a species, her important work in bringing out the probable material bases for the divergence from the apes and the emergence of processes of cultural change (stemming from the gathering innovation) helps to make clear that there is no basis whatsoever to consider that such things as the oppression of women, of classes, or of entire nations and drives to war are, or have ever been, expressions of some biologically mandated "human nature" (or of "Mother Nature being sexist"—to quote E.O. Wilson). "Ironically," writes Tanner, "it was the development of culture that made elaboration or dichotomization possible in any direction; a lopsided society such as ours that either ignores or infantilizes half the species— women—can exist" (p. 277).

What really stands out is the single most distinguishing feature of our evolutionary line: that our biology *itself* set the basis for an ever-increasing reliance on our active transformation of external conditions and an increasing capacity to respond with great flexibility to changes in these conditions, including those wrought by humans themselves. The transmission of learned material and the development of social memory has made it possible for each succeeding generation of human beings to further enhance the human ability to transform the external world. Thus even *our very biology*—as well as all of human *history*—stands as a refutation and indictment of all the various brands of biodeterminist views of human social relations which are repeatedly used to excuse and justify everything from rape to wars of plunder and, more subtly perhaps, to conceal the actual processes of historical development through class societies, and the actual bases of oppressive social orders—thereby retarding their full uprooting.[23]

---

[23]A common related misconception, for instance, is the view that all social oppression originated with the first use of "force" to subjugate other human beings. But as Engels pointed out in his polemics against Dühring (who felt that "force" was the original sin which perverted all future history), it was necessary from the time of the earliest subjugation of one group of humans by another for the subjugator to have the means of production with which to employ the subjugated, and the means to assure the latter's subsistence. Thus there must have been some form of *property* which "must have been obtained by labour before there was any possibility of its being robbed" (Engels 1878, p. 206). And even though, as Marx put it (1859, p. 28) "In the case of the slave the instrument of production is stolen directly," there must be some surplus available with which to sustain this slave, not to mention the production of weapons with which to subjugate him. As Marx so succinctly put it, "[I]n order to be able to plunder, there must be something to plunder, consequently production" (1859, p. 28).

III

It is sobering to recall that the material origins of the subordinate social status of half the human species throughout recorded history was not posed as a question, nor certainly deemed worthy of serious investigation, until the middle of the 19th century. Karl Marx and Frederick Engels cut through the societal prejudice of their time to insist that the subordinate position of women had nothing to do with either some innate deficiencies of female nature or any divine decrees (or "natural features") sanctifying this order of things. They maintained, instead, that the oppression of women was a product and consequence of the social organization of human beings, basically determined in any given society by the particular level of development of the productive forces and the corresponding set of production relations. Linking the social status of women to the division of labor and to the relations of ownership and distribution of property prevailing in any given time and society naturally raised some questions about just how permanent this set-up could be. These were certainly not the mainstream ideas of the period.

Engels points out, for instance, that before the 1860s there had been no attempts to study the history of the family: it was taken for granted that the patriarchal form of the family had always existed and indeed existed in the form of the modern European bourgeois family—"as if the family had really experienced no historical development at all" (1884, p. 75). Scattered bits of information on the existence of polygamy or polyandry in non-European cultures tended to be dismissed as aberrant oddities, as compared to the supposedly more natural form of monogamy. "In this field, the science of history," writes Engels, "was still completely under the influence of the Five Books of Moses" (1884, pp. 74-75). The very notion that in primitive times the relations between the sexes might have been much less constrained, and that (sacrilege, oh sacrilege) a woman might routinely engage in sexual relations with a number of men, was deemed so horrifying that there were frequent attempts to show that monogamy was the natural order of things, not just in the human species, but among vertebrates more generally. Much was made, for instance, of the fact that many species of birds exhibit monogamous pairings of long duration. All this prompted the following delightful reply from Engels: "[E]xamples of faithful monogamy among birds prove nothing about man for the simple reason that men are not descended from birds. And if strict monogamy is the height of all virtue, then the palm must go to the tapeworm, which has a complete set of male and female sexual organs in each of its 50 to 200 proglottides or sections, and spends its whole life copulating in all its sections with itself" (1884, p. 98).

While almost no information on the evolutionary origins of the human species or on its earliest forms of social organization was available in Engels's day, he recognized that no social institutions existed in a vacuum, free from interconnection with historical antecedents. He was therefore quick to recognize the importance of a largely ignored work published in 1861 by the German scholar Bachofen, entitled *Mutterrecht (Mother Right)*. By delving into the literature of the classical Roman and Greek civilizations (such as Aeschylus's *Oresteia*), Bachofen had been to document a radical change in the social organization of these societies: it seemed that they had initially been organized on the basis of "mother right," i.e., that individuals had traced their descent through their mothers rather than their fathers and had inherited from that side as well. Bachofen concluded that the women of this period were therefore very influential and in fact ruled the societies. At some point, corresponding to the advent of the classical heroic age, the system of mother right had apparently been overthrown and replaced by a system in which descent was traced through the father, social status was inherited through the males, etc. This change seemed to coincide with the apparent introduction of enforced monogamy to control the reproductive activity of the women and remove doubts as to the paternity of any given child.

This was an extremely important discovery, but Bachofen was not able to determine the causes of such a radical transformation. He observed that these changes coincided with important changes in the religious beliefs of the times (as the literature records that some gods were "overthrown" by others at the time) and thought that therein lay the cause of the social upheaval. Engels, on the other hand, understood that changes in the religious sphere could only reflect changes in the material conditions of life in these societies, and that this was where one must look to discover the causes of the apparent overthrow of mother right.

Then in 1871 Lewis Henry Morgan, an anthropologist working among various North American Indian

tribes, compiled vast amounts of field data on the activities and forms of social organization of these various
peoples. What emerged from his data was the suggestion
that, in societies with little in the way of means of production, the basic form of social organization was what
Morgan called the *gens*, a relatively small group of individuals who were related to each other through their
mothers' lines. Membership in a gens typically entailed
obligations of cooperation and support vis-à-vis other
members of the gens. Women often seemed to be influential in decision making, and their lineages served as
mainstays of social organization. Marriage often seemed
to occur within a tribe (made up of a number of distinct
clans, or gentes) but outside the gens, with the man
often coming to join his wife's clan rather than the other
way around.[24]

Morgan observed many different societies (and obtained indirect evidence about primitive societies in
many parts of the world). He included in his work
descriptions of societies which had expanded to form not
only tribes made up of matrilineal clans but also in some
cases greater confederacies involving a number of tribes
which required the establishment of more complex
forms of governance such as tribal councils, councils of
chiefs, etc. Wherever the system of descent through the

---

[24]Such marriage outside the gens would objectively help to prevent
problems of inbreeding, although this is not likely to have been
consciously understood in ancient times. The custom of encourag-
ing marriage outside the small group of related individuals may
well have simply come about as the natural consequence of a
desire to continually expand the clan's sphere of social relations,
including forging new ties of mutual help, etc., with individuals
from other groups. When Margaret Mead once asked an Arapesh
man why his people disapproved of sexual relations with a sister he
replied: "What is the matter with you? Sleep with your sister? But
don't you want a brother-in-law? With whom will you garden,
with whom will you hunt, with whom will you visit?" (cited in
Leacock, introduction to Engels 1884, p. 27).

mother prevailed, women seemed to have high social status in the community, an equal voice in decision making on major social issues, and sometimes even the right to elect and/or depose male chieftains where such structures existed. For instance, Morgan records the following observations made by a missionary who lived among the Iroquois Senecas:

> As to their family system, when occupying the old long houses [communistic households comprising several families], it is probable that some one clan [gens] predominated, the women taking in husbands, however, from the other clans [gentes].... Usually, the female portion ruled the house.... The stores were in common; but woe to the luckless husband or lover who was too shiftless to do his share of the providing. No matter how many children, or whatever goods he might have in the house, he might at any time be ordered to pick up his blanket and budge; and after such orders it would not be healthful for him to attempt to disobey. The house would be too hot for him; and...he must retreat to his own clan [gens]; or, as was often done, go and start a new matrimonial alliance in some other. The women were the great power among the clans [gentes], as everywhere else. They did not hesitate, when occasion required, "to knock off the horns," as it was technically called, from the head of a chief, and send him back to the ranks of the warriors. (Morgan, cited in Engels 1884, p. 113, bracketed comments by Engels)

While Morgan was generally treated as a pariah in anthropological circles, Marx and Engels welcomed his vast amounts of data which helped to shake up what Engels called "one of the most absurd notions taken over from 18th century enlightenment...that in the beginning of society woman was the slave of man" (p. 113).

In addition to information on the high status of

women in many of the societies he studied, Morgan reported that some of these societies seemed to be undergoing a dramatic change away from reckoning descent through the mother's line to doing it through the father's, thereby replacing the old "matriarchal gens" as Morgan called it, with a "patriarchal" gens. This transformation, which Morgan reported but could not clearly explain, led Engels to exclaim that "This rediscovery of the primitive matriarchal gens as the earlier stage of the patriarchal gens of civilized peoples has the same importance for anthropology as Darwin's theory of evolution has for biology and Marx's theory of surplus value for political economy" (1884, p. 83). Here, then, was data from living peoples which tended to corroborate some of the discoveries made by Bachofen in sifting through the literature of the classical Romans and Greeks! Morgan's discoveries were so important because they provided the first direct clues that relations between the sexes (reflected in marriage forms, relative social influence, etc.) were not unchanging but tended to vary, and in a way which seemed to correlate with the level of development of the productive base of a given society.

As Engels worked to further distill the vast amounts of data recorded by Morgan, the picture which began to emerge was one in which the role and position of women relative to men dramatically changes as a society expands its sphere of productive activities further and further away from the simplest acquisition of natural products. Engels adopts Morgan's distinctions between three basic types of societies: those based on the simple acquisition of resources in their natural state (what we would now call gatherer-hunter or foraging societies); those engaging in a further expansion of the resource base through the domestication of animals and/or the cultivation of plants; and those engaging in industrial production and the production of goods for exchange.

Like any initial attempt at scientific classification (such as the Linnaean system of classification of plant and animal species for instance), Morgan and Engels's breakdown can be faulted for being somewhat rigid; the categories are altogether too neat and self-circumscribed, with little of the overlap and mixed-bag character which is the stuff of life. One can also object to the assumption that all human societies follow the same straight-line progression through each of these stages in inevitable succession.

Yet despite these obvious limitations (including the fact that Morgan sometimes presents fairly distorted views of societies which did not exactly fit into one neat category), the fact remains that this early attempt to correlate forms of social organization with major differences in the *productive activities* of different societies provided (much like the Linnaean system) a frame of reference, a tool of initial systematization, a basic scaffolding on which further knowledge could be accumulated and adjustments made. In fact, in light of information available today, and placing the work in its historical context, Engels's treatment of these questions in *The Origin of the Family, Private Property, and the State* seems remarkably insightful in its essential features— especially in contrast to so many stubbornly idealist attempts to seek the bases for human social relations, institutions, and ideologies in half-baked theories of "human nature" and everywhere else *except* in the sphere of productive activities which are the underpinning of any society.[25]

---

[25]Even those who correctly combat notions of an innate, biologically determined human nature, such as many of the cultural anthropologists, could learn a great deal from Engels's approach, and in particular would do well to get a better handle on historical materialism so as to bring out not only the great cultural diversity of human social systems, but also the more universal patterns of

   While this essay cannot attempt to discuss Engels's
theses on the sequence of changes in human social
organization once distinct classes and a state apparatus
had clearly emerged (such as in societies based on
slavery, feudalism, or capitalist commodity relations),
some of his thinking concerning the earliest forms of
human social organization does fall within the scope of
this book. Again, basing himself largely on Morgan's
work, from which he was attempting to distill some
basic historical principles, Engels suggested that the
earliest forms of human social organization were
characterized by the appropriation of resources in their
natural state with little development of productive
forces beyond simple tools and weapons. Small groups of
related individuals reckoned their common lineage
through their mothers; women would therefore have
high social status and be very influential in making decisions affecting the whole of society. Engels postulates
that relations between men and women in such a society
would have first taken the form of group marriages in the
sense that a man could have sexual relations with a large
number of women and a woman with a large number of
men.[26] In such systems women and men would likely

---

development and change. By uncovering the intimate connection
between the material base of a society (how resources are obtained,
transformed, etc.) and the social relations characterizing that
society, Engels's historical materialist approach opens the door to
an understanding of both the origins of various social systems and
the factors which serve as an impetus for *change* from one system
to another.

[26]Here it should be noted that kinship terminologies in some
societies studied by Morgan and others which suggest that each
man and woman was "married" to many partners are misleading
because what is more likely being indicated is the fact that relations are *permitted* with the large pool of partners, though not
necessarily put into practice. Similarly, kinship terms used in
many systems do not necessarily correspond to the actual degree of
biological relatedness, as when all one's mothers' sisters'
daughters are considered one's own sisters, etc.

have been able to choose, or to leave, their partners with a minimum of fuss and societal interference.

But as the productive base of the society expanded (as with the beginnings of plant and animal domestication), relations between men and women clearly became more restrictive and regulated. Marriages were increasingly arranged by relatives with an eye to expanding networks of mutual obligation and political alliances and to securing more wealth (marriages were often cemented by exchanges of goods—such as cattle—between concerned families). At first such "pairing marriages" would still have been relatively easy to terminate, but this too would change as the relations between partners became increasingly intertwined with nascent property relations. Engels reasons that, prior to society's ability to accumulate surpluses of goods, the acquisition of food resources would have been a communal undertaking; although a division of labor would have occurred along sexual lines, if only in relation to the production of children. (Engels, it should be noted, goes beyond that, incorrectly assuming that men were the primary providers of food in foraging societies.) But Engels postulates that with the ability to expand the productive base of the society and the parceling of property among individuals—which would have been instituted for more efficient exploitation of herd and crop resources—ownership and distribution would have fallen preferentially into the hands of the men. At this point the question of inheritance of the newly generated surpluses would begin to pose itself and to stand in contradiction to the practice of establishing lines of descent and networks of social obligation and cooperation through the women, since the women were becoming increasingly divorced from the principal activities involved in generating these surpluses.

From this contradiction, then, would stem the need to replace old kinship systems centered on women with new ones centered on men, and the women who did not control the ownership and distribution of the newly accumulating resources stood to lose much social status and decision-making power. Engels suggests that men would want to pass on the new wealth to their own children, making proof of paternity an issue for the first time in history: the sexual activity of women would be increasingly regulated, making it more difficult for them to freely choose or leave a man, or to have more than one sexual partner. Eventually, strict monogamy might be imposed (always "for the woman but not for the man," as Engels points out) to more fully control the reproductive activity of the women and determine the paternity of the children with greater certainty. Means of enforcing monogamy on the women would range from simple pressure to conform to starvation or execution for breaking the rules. The use of chastity belts; intricate bookkeeping devices to record the exact timing of sexual encounters; the castration of men to serve as reliable eunuch guardians of harems; the widespread practice of clitoridectomies[27] (cutting out the clitoris of young girls, sometimes accompanied by a further procedure to sew the vagina closed) to decrease or eliminate sexual pleasure in order to keep women from "straying" with men other than their assigned husbands: all of these were means of ensuring that the patrimony would not be squandered on someone else's children.[28]

---

[27]The practice of clitoridectomy is still prevalent in some parts of the world: some recent estimates suggest that more than 20 million women and girls alive today have been subjected to this practice (cf. Hrdy 1981, pp. 178, 183-84 and contained references).

[28]Of course none of the methods for the forcible imposition of monogamy on women are foolproof, and it therefore remained for the property holders of the enlightened bourgeois era to resolve the issue with typical pragmatic panache. The smooth preservation and perpetuation of property relations could be ensured by cosmetic decree: Engels tells us that the Code Napoleon declared

While Engels necessarily had to be fairly speculative about the basic forms of social organization and relations between the sexes in societies which were devoid of property and social stratification, the world historical record since that time speaks for itself. Through all its twists and turns, the history of the family—the institutionalized form for the relations between the sexes—has been intimately intertwined with the oppression and subjugation of whole sections of humanity.[29] And for women especially, the family has constituted a veritable Trail of Tears throughout its entire history and to this very day.

Interestingly, Engels's historical materialist approach to the history of change in human social organization has been increasingly substantiated in light of the accumulating scientific evidence. The central role of females in the social organization of many primate species, among which are some of our closest primate relatives (as reflected, for instance, in the fact that females are the social focus of chimpanzee troops, frequently initiate sexual relations, etc.), admittedly says little about early social organization in *Homo sapiens,*

---

simply, "L'enfant conçu pendant le mariage a pour père le mari" (1884, p. 131): the father of a child conceived during marriage is—the husband! Et voilà!

[29]In fact, the very origin of the word "family" reveals this association. Engels writes:

> The original meaning of the word "family" (*familia*) is not that compound of sentimentality and domestic strife which forms the ideal of the present-day philistine; among the Romans it did not at first even refer to the married pair and their children but only to the slaves. *Famulus* means domestic slave, and *familia* is the total number of slaves belonging to one man. As late as the time of Gaius, the *familia, id est patrimonium* (family, that is, the patrimony, the inheritance) was bequeathed by will. The term was invented by the Romans to denote a new social organism whose head ruled over wife and children and a number of slaves, and was invested under Roman paternal power with rights of life and death over them all. (Engels 1884, p. 121)

whose capacity for rapid learning and incessant re-structuring of its social and natural environment makes it difficult to say what, if any, features of ancestral social organization may have been preserved through the hominid line and up to our own single remaining hominid species (whose clear presence in the fossil record is traced to at least 100,000 years ago). But, at the least, comparative primatology and attempts to recreate possible evolutionary pathways from the time of the ape-hominid divergence can help to shatter androcentric, biodeterminist views by bringing out that it is at minimum quite conceivable that the hominid line started off with a form of social organization made up of fluid groupings rather than rigid hierarchies and in which females may well have been essential determinants of social organization. What happened to hominid social organization in the millions of years since the divergence is still almost completely shrouded in mystery and will probably never be well understood, but notions that the entire period was characterized by one single unchanging social pattern are almost certainly wrong: the differences in modes of food acquisition which have been suggested for the different *Australopithecines* may well have been reflected in differences of social organization, and surely even new innovation in the hominids' abilities to interpret and transform the outside world could not have come about without inducing jolts and strains in the hominids' way of life. Imagine, for instance, the social polarization which must have occurred in these early groupings around the question of the use, and later manufacture, of fire! Most likely some must have opposed this change, been frightened by it, resisted it, or been cowed by it, while other more pioneering sorts made use of it, expanding the productive base of the society, rendering large quantities of meat and tough-fibered plants more digestible and extending its use to repelling predators, facilitating establishment in cold zones, exploring its possible ritual uses, etc.

While these millennia were surely not static, there is, however, no doubt that the pace of social change would appear to us to have been excruciatingly slow. This is to be expected from the low level of development of productive forces and the therefore still very limited capacity for radical transformations of the outside world. Frankly, these millenia must have been characterized by continuous struggle to avoid extinction, which on a local level must not always have been successful. And yet out of all this a single species emerged which managed to spread itself out all across the planet and successfully establish itself under the most variable of conditions. Modern *Homo sapiens* flourished in its different corners of the globe, bringing forth an amazing diversity of cultural forms: extremely varied languages, art forms, religious beliefs, etc. And yet the findings of modern anthropology and related sciences reveal certain patterns which seem to cut across cultural and geographic lines; these patterns are the main forms of social organization which time and again seem to correlate with a particular productive base.

While Engels's *The Origin of the Family, Private Property, and the State* is surely not correct in all its details, some of his most key assumptions concerning human social organization seem increasingly justified:

That early social organization was primarily communal, as there would not at first have been a basis for material accumulation and the parceling of means of production in the form of private property, and there would therefore not have been social distinctions based on property differentials (such as the first classes in Rome which were defined in relation to the number of asses owned by individuals), or special bodies of governance standing outside and above the masses of the people (political institutions, a state apparatus) serving to regulate the ownership, distribution, defense, and expansion of property;

That the social status of women would not typically be inferior to that of men in such societies, due to an apparently universal method of basing social rights and obligations on degrees of relatedness which were most surely and naturally established through women, a situation which most likely ensured the women an influential voice in all affairs of the society, equal if not superior to that of men, and which would most likely have persisted in the absence of the accumulation of surpluses which could become differentially concentrated in the hands of one sex;

That even in the absence of social stratification (such as hierarchies or classes) a division of labor would necessarily have existed in the earliest human social systems and that it would have fallen out along sexual lines and have been linked to the propagation of children;

That in cases where the productive base of society expanded sufficiently to require the parceling of the ownership of the means of production, and where the ownership and distribution of property fell into the hands of the men, social divisions based on differential control and ownership of property would emerge, and decision-making powers would fall preferentially to those having the greatest control over the means of production; where the women had little or no control over the principal means of production (as a consequence of the prior division of labor), they would be shoved out of the decision-making sphere and relegated to inferior social status—the complex lines of duties and obligations of mutual help traced through maternal lines would be abolished or become irrelevant as they were superceded by the new property relations.

Engels's view, taken from Morgan, that the earliest forms of society were typified by the matriarchal gens (later to be replaced by the patriarchal gens) has remained controversial. For one thing the use of the terms matriarchal and patriarchal is misleading: they have a connotation of political power which would be meaningless in the absence of property relations and distinct governing bodies standing above the mass of society. In primitive communal systems, the typically small groupings of people can make all necessary social decisions through a process of general discussion and consensus of all the women and men of the society. It is therefore unlikely that early human societies were "matriarchal" in the sense of being "run" by women.

Nevertheless, it is true that systems in which individuals trace their descent through their mother's line or where women serve to anchor the group—as when a man comes to live with his wife's group rather than the other way around—have proven to be extremely common among peoples in basic foraging societies. In some cases there seems to be a bilateral system whereby relatives are traced through both parents, although men may still be expected to join their wife's group and social obligations may still be determined through the woman's side. This is true, for instance, among the !Kung, where relatives on both sides are referred to, though the man typically comes to live with his wife and her relatives at least for a number of years, and is expected to provide meat for them during that time. Therefore, the words "matrifocal" and "matrilineal" more correctly describe the systems of establishing residency or computing descent and associated obligations through the women—all of which Morgan and Engels lumped under the term matriarchy.

It should also be pointed out that descent through the mother does not necessarily mean inheritance through the mother in the classical sense, since in the absence of individual property there may be nothing to inherit. What seems to precede the concept and practice of inheritance of individual property is the "inheritance" of sets of social rights and obligations determined by kinship ties and often held in common by all members of a particular group (such as the "right" to use the plants, animals, and water in a particular area, or the obligations of mutual help with others in your kinship group). In some foraging societies this type of "inheritance" (use of the land) is apparently sometimes passed on through the mothers, sometimes through the fathers. It is unclear whether such a fluid and mixed system might represent a common ancestral form of organization or whether it is simply reflective of a transition away from matrilineality, perhaps largely due, as in the !Kung, to a breakup of the old ways of life through contact and exchange with herding or agricultural peoples and the encroachment of modern-day commodity relations. On a global scale there can be little doubt, however, of the extreme prevalence of matrilineal systems in foraging societies. Beyond that, whether or not matrilineal systems were universal in *all* primitive societies, the fact remains that *transitions* from matrilineality to patrilineality (and patriarchy) have been documented in many societies with the emergence of expanded means of production differentially controlled by the men, and owned on an individualized basis.

Before this point the question of individualized inheritance of means of production would not pose itself, and therefore society would not concern itself with correctly identifying the father of any particular child. The mother's identity would be evident and would suffice to insure a child a place in a particular clan. Children would be free of the stamp of property and would not be treated as such and, at least past the nursing stage, would most likely be seen as members of the entire community and be dealt with collectively to a large extent, as is in fact the case in many foraging societies in the world today. In this respect, it is interesting to note the exchange between a 17th-century Jesuit missionary and a man of the

Naskapi tribe of hunter-gatherers, as reported by Eleanor Leacock in her introduction to Engels's *The Origin of the Family, Private Property, and the State* (p. 38):

> Seventeenth century Jesuit missionaries writing of their experiences state that "the women have great power here" and that "the choice of plans, of undertakings, of journeys, of winterings, lies in nearly every instance in the hands of the housewife". A Jesuit scolds a man for not being "the master," telling him "in France women do not rule their husbands". To make the women obey their husbands became one of the concerns of the missionaries, particularly in relation to the sexual freedom that obtained: "I told him that it was not honorable for a woman to love anyone else except her husband, and that, this evil being among them (women's sexual freedom) he himself was not sure that his son, who was there present, was his son." The Naskapi's reply is telling: "Thou hast no sense. You French people love only your own children; but we love all the children of our tribe."

There would clearly not have been any basis for a division of human societies into oppressors and oppressed without a prior accumulation of some kind of surplus. Even occasional killings of individuals among the ancestral apes or transitional hominids would have little, if anything, to do with the later emergence of *social* subjugation of individuals kept alive, a development only made possible by the existence of a material surplus. The availability of some kind of surplus was in fact a great spur to the development of all human activity not related in the most direct and narrow sense to immediate subsistence (such as art, religion, and political institutions), as well as a further development of productive forces and activities.

Once the gathering innovation had become well established, the basis had been laid for further developments in the methods of food location and acquisition. Indeed, the significant structural biological reorganization which seems to have been involved in the emergence of full bipedality (including such other neotenic features as the late closure of skull sutures allowing for postnatal brain expansion and the prolonged periods of juvenility) made possible an as yet unprecedented degree of interaction between the early hominids and the external environments which they could increasingly affect and transform and which, in turn, continually reacted back upon them, spurring further mental integration, communication and learning. To the earliest tools—the hands, but also probably gathering implements such as digging sticks and natural containers—were eventually added somewhat more sophisticated modified stone implements suitable for butchering carcasses, and later, the first stone hunting implements. Later still, the capacity to use (and produce) fire would make possible the cooking of many tough plant foods and large amounts of meat, rendering them more digestible, a development which no doubt had far-reaching and immediate implications for social organization and the further development of productive forces.[30] But even hunting with weapons could not have emerged without a signifi-

---

[30]The relative timing of the emergence of hunting with weapons and the use of fire is not clear. Tanner reports (p. 240) that fossil remains indicate the occurrence of a crude form of butchery of animal carcasses with stone tools around 1.7 million years ago, but suggests that this did not yet represent an ability to bring down large animals with weapons (although it is possible that big animals may have been hunted and killed by driving them over cliffs or into bogs where they could then be butchered, a technique used during the last Ice Age and in recent history by hunting tribes). The use of fire dates back to around a million years ago by most current estimates, although there is some suggestion that it may have been used in Kenya as long as 1.5 million years ago. It is of course quite possible that the ability to use fire was closely associated with the development of more large-scale hunting, as it could have been used to frighten and stampede game animals and

cant prior capacity for ensuring a surplus of food beyond what was needed for on-the-spot consumption by individual foragers; only this would make it possible for some sections of a population to engage in activities which were not immediately productive. This is largely because hunting, unlike gathering, is a very unpredictable activity which often involves many days of fruitless search for prey and which demands significant energy expenditures on the part of the hunter, regardless of failure or success in obtaining meat. The accumulation through gathering of a food supply on a regular basis, and the regular sharing of these foods, would make it possible for some individuals in a population to go off

---

would have enabled the consumption of much greater amounts of meat rendered more digestible through cooking.

It would also have permitted those using fire to expand into colder zones of the planet. For a long time, fire was obtained from natural sources (such as lightning) and stored and transported in the form of live coals or smoldering wood, but it was apparently not regularly manufactured (i.e., ignited by people) until comparatively recently. While some of the oldest wooden fire-starting implements may well have decomposed and be forever lost, it is significant that the oldest archeological finds of reliable fire-starting tools (such as wooden fire drills) date back only to about 9,000 years ago and that simple flint starters appear only around 7,000 years ago. Despite the lack of evidence, it has been suggested that full knowledge of fire making must go back at least 50,000 years to the last Ice Age; whether or not this is true, it is clear that for a very long time it must have been easier to store and carry fire than to ignite it intermittently.

Fire probably played an important role in the domestication of plants and animals: to this day in many primitive societies (including the !Kung) brush fires are set to create clearings which attract game animals coming to feed on the new plant growth; such methods may have been used to attract and capture the originators of the first domesticated herds. Similarly, slash-and-burn agriculture (through which small clearings are created in forested areas by cutting and burning trees, which clears the ground and provides a layer of fertile ash) continues to be a common method for creating small garden plots characterizing much of tropical subsistence agriculture

hunting for days at a time without their survival or the survival of any other individuals being directly dependent on the success of any particular hunting venture.

To better appreciate how crucial it is for the main food supply of a group of humans without developed productive forces to come from gathered foods, it is worthwhile to look at present-day gatherer-hunters such as the !Kung. Although the !Kung are amazingly knowledgeable about details of the environment they live in and make use of snares and bows with arrows dipped in poison to kill their prey, hunters still only average one kill in four days of hunting; during the 15 or so years of their most productive hunting periods, individual !Kung men walk between 1,200 and 2,100 miles a year in pursuit of game. Most hunters alternate periods of intense hunting with long periods of relative inactivity, and the basic subsistence of all individuals in the society is therefore ensured by daily gathering of plant foods, which is accomplished primarily, if not exclusively, by the women. !Kung women contribute 60 to 80 percent of the total food by weight consumed in their societies; meat supplies provided by the men are extremely variable, but average out to 20 to 40 percent (cf. Shostak 1981, p. 12; Lee 1979, p. 450).

Very similar patterns of food acquisition and of division of labor between the sexes have been reported for gatherer-hunter societies in many different parts of the globe, ranging from the Kalahari Desert in Africa to the Amazonian rain forests. While they all have their own cultural specificities, most traditional gatherer-hunter societies have many features in common: they rely primarily on gathering of plant foods for basic subsistence, while hunting provides the rarer, less reliable, but much-valued meat supplements; they have tremendously detailed knowledge of the environments in which they live and rich cultural traditions, but minimal development of productive forces, typically using only a limited set of collecting instruments like digging sticks and hunting implements such as bows and arrows, simple snares, and plant poisons; they do not accumulate any significant possessions and typically, broadly, and routinely *share* food supplies and what little else they may have; they tend to live in relatively small groups of fluctuating composition and generally fairly fluid social organization; some exhibit beginning social hierarchies, but others have no formal leaders or governing bodies of any sort. All, however, have some form of division of labor in the society, even though it may not be very rigidly defined, and this division of labor seems to fall out primarily along sex lines. And while some of these societies may at first glance be striking in the apparent degree of ''equality'' between the men and women, there seems to be a connection between the basic division of labor and certain seemingly incipient, embryonic forms of social inequities between the sexes.

The much-studied !Kung gatherer-hunters are a case in point. While !Kung societies have been undergoing extremely rapid changes in recent years due to more regular interaction with people from pastoral, horticultural, and industrial societies, they have until very recently maintained a traditional gatherer-hunter way of life. The traditional !Kung have no formal leaders, headmen, tribal councils, or any other ruling bodies; they typically live in such small nomadic bands that major decisions concerning their way of life are reached through general discussion, involving adults of both sexes, until a consensus is achieved; certain individuals play more leading roles than others in such discussions, but this seems to be on the basis of generally acknowledged experience and wisdom (often tied to greater age) and is not dependent on formal titles or positions. The traditional !Kung have very little in the way of material possessions, which consist mainly of items directly related to subsistence activities such as digging sticks, bows and arrows, and water containers, with the few items such as pipes, beads, children's toys, or musical instruments circulating continuously in "gift-giving networks": "The total weight of an individual's personal property is less than 12 kg and can easily be carried from place to place" (Lee 1979, p. 456). Similarly the !Kung do not store food for any length of time:

> . . . [they] make no sharp dichotomy between the resources of the natural environment and the social wealth. The unimproved land itself is the means of production, and because it is owned by no one exclusively, it is available to everyone who can use it. The !Kung do not amass a surplus because they conceive of the environment itself as their storehouse. . . .
>
> Because they know what to expect from the environment, they see little point in bringing food and raw materials to camp before they are actually needed. The food collected by the members of a camp is distributed and consumed without delay within the boundaries of the camp or by the camp's immediate neighbors. (Lee 1979, p. 455)

Significantly, then, ownership is necessarily a barely emergent concept among the !Kung, being limited to the recognition of certain regions being "owned" by living descendants—both men and women—of those people who have been there the longest. It seems to have limited social implications, meaning simply that visitors to an area are supposed to ask the owners for permission to gather plants, water, and game in the area; in traditional !Kung society this is largely a formality as permission is rarely, if ever, denied, but it ensures that the visitors will reciprocate whenever the occasion comes up. Such reciprocal ties among the !Kung are the norm, not the exception, and in fact regular sharing of resources seems to be universal among foraging peoples.

Among the !Kung the worst possible insult is to accuse someone of "stinginess." The culprit is constantly teased and goaded until he or she complies with the social norm, thereby effectively preventing any differential accumulation within the society. Observing this has prompted Richard Lee to point out that although sharing obviously has to be learned and any child is born with the capacity for both sharing and selfishness:

> The fact that communal sharing of food resources has been directly observed in recent years among the !Kung and dozens of other foraging groups is a finding that should not be glossed over lightly. Its universality among foragers lends strong support to the theory of Marx and Engels that a stage of primitive communism prevailed before the rise of the state and the breakup of society into classes (Engels 1884). One should add the proviso, however, that this communism does not extend, as far as we know, to include sexual rights, as Marx and Engels, following Morgan (1877), originally believed. (Lee 1979, p. 460)

The fact is that the role of women in traditional gatherer-hunter societies such as the !Kung is contradictory, as revealed by the following:

> Does women's predominant role in production, their leverage in marriage, and their sharing of core group membership with men lead to power in the political arena as well? The answer in a broad sense is yes: !Kung women's participation in group discussions and decision making is probably greater than that of women in most tribal, peasant, and industrial societies. . . . But the level of their participation is not equal to that of men. The latter appear to do about two-thirds of the talking in discussions involving both sexes, and men act as group spokespersons far more frequently than do women. . . . (Lee 1979)

And:

> Women's status in the community is high and their
> influence considerable. They are often prominent in
> major family and band decisions, such as where and
> when to move and whom their children will marry.
> Many also share core leadership in a band and owner-
> ship of water holes and foraging areas. Just how in-
> fluential they really are and how their status com-
> pares with that of men is a complicated question:
> women may, in fact, be nearly equal to men, but the
> culture seems to *define* them as less powerful. In
> other words, their influence may be greater than the
> !Kung—of either sex—like to admit. (Shostak 1981,
> p. 13)

The fact that studies of gatherer-hunter societies
reveal that—despite their primitive communal mode of
production—men and women seem to differ somewhat
in social status has led the sociobiology types to loudly
proclaim that surely *this* must be proof of an innate
biological basis for the contradictions between the sexes.
"The question of interest, then, is the extent to which
the *hereditary* qualities of hunter-gatherer existence
have influenced the course of subsequent cultural evolution," writes E.O. Wilson in *On Human Nature* (p. 88,
emphasis added). In an absolutely astounding combination of idealism and metaphysics, Wilson goes on to
develop his views: "I believe that the influence has been
substantial. *In evidence* is the fact that the emergence of
civilization has everywhere followed a definable sequence" (p. 91, emphasis added).

Thus, according to Wilson, parallels in the sequence
of forms of social organization in different parts of the
world (such as transitions from gatherer-hunter systems
to more hierarchical tribes and chiefdoms, to cities and
states and the emergence of class structures) become
proof that all human social history must be conditioned

by a common biological blueprint without which it would be impossible to explain such similarities! There is not a single hint here that similarities of production relations based on similar levels of development of productive forces might account for these parallelisms.[31]

Of course one might be tempted to ask why then these social structures ever bothered to evolve from the original blueprint and undergo the evident major transformations. Wilson's answer is basically that things in nature grow, and sometimes even go a little out of whack, to wit:

> In my opinion the key to the emergence of civilization is *hypertrophy*, the extreme growth of preexisting structures. Like the teeth of the baby elephant that lengthen into tusks, and the cranial bones of the male elk that sprout into astonishing great antlers, the basic social responses of the hunter-gatherers have metamorphosed from relatively modest environmental adaptations into unexpectedly elaborate, even monstrous forms in more advanced societies. Yet the directions this change can take and its final products are constrained by the genetically influenced behavioral predispositions that constituted the earlier, simpler adaptations of preliterate human beings. (pp. 94-95)

Thus, as Wilson would have it, small genetic differences between men and women blossomed into the full-scale subjugation of women, and similar preexisting biological bases grew into full-scale racism, nationalism, war, etc. Of course, while recognizing that we are not exclusively tied to our genetic programs, Wilson does feel compelled to remind us that we should be realistic as to

---

[31]For a diametrically opposed viewpoint and clear exposition of the historical materialist viewpoint, cf. Avakian's *For a Harvest of Dragons*, Chapter I, especially part 4, "Marxism as science and in contrast to previous and opposing worldviews."

the degree and rate at which we can expect to get rid of some of these problems. After all, Wilson is essentially saying, you can't fool Mother Nature!

But a closer examination of gatherer-hunter societies and the actual relationship between the incipient inequalities in them and later, more full-blown social inequalities and antagonisms, reveals a different process at work, with different motive forces. For example, more recent information about social organization of various present-day peoples living in basic subsistence economies, i.e., by gathering and hunting—with the use of but a few simple tools and weapons and little or no development of property relations—provides us with valuable clues concerning not only the probable earliest forms of human social organization, but also the factors mediating major transformations in this organization.

The !Kung and other gatherer-hunters may not have classes or even strict social hierarchies, but they do have a division of labor. Both men and women can and do gather plant foods, but this activity is mainly engaged in by the women who supply the great bulk of the subsistence plant foods consumed in the society. But, *typically*, women in gatherer-hunter societies do not hunt. This is not due to a female inability to locate game or handle weapons, or to some other fundamental difference having a "genetic origin," as was preposterously suggested by E.O. Wilson (cf. quote opening this essay). In fact it is possible to find exceptions to this general pattern in almost every foraging society. For instance Shostak (1981) cites a case among the !Kung where a middle-aged woman whose husband was deemed "lazy" in obtaining meat and who craved such food took up hunting and became proficient in this activity, although most people considered her somewhat eccentric. Tanner (1981) cites similar instances.[32] In quite a few foraging

---

[32]In the 1930s, anthropologist Regina Flannery noted that some

societies women routinely capture small animals or locate a carcass they can scavenge. Significantly, this is usually done in the course of their gathering activities and within the geographical range normally covered in one day's foraging. There have also been instances of collective hunting involving men, women, and children in such activities as rabbit hunts, again usually in close proximity to base camps. The specifics of the division of labor among foragers obviously varies somewhat according to the types of food available, their relative abundance and seasonal availability, and takes into account such things as the size, local abundance, and degree of mobility of game species, the degree to which the hunt had to be fast-paced and quiet, etc. The point is not that women cannot hunt, or that they absolutely never hunt in foraging societies. But it is an undeniable fact that the most common distinction in the activities of men and women in such societies in all parts of the world is that between gathering (mainly done by women) and hunting (almost exclusively done by men). This distinction is likely to have originated as a natural division of labor which was spontaneously instituted and agreed upon by both sexes, simply because in most cases it makes little sense for adult women to engage in hunting: women bear the children for long months and then typically nurse them at the breast not for a few weeks or months but for a number of *years* (three years is typical among the !Kung) before they can be sufficiently sustained solely on gathered foods; the weaning of one child is typically initiated in the beginning of pregnancy with another. Women in such societies can and do engage in much productive gathering and carry very heavy loads

---

Cree women who had been "forced by circumstance" to engage in hunting had reputations as good hunters. She also reported that, among the Mescalero Apache, "young married women might go hunting with their husbands" (Flannery 1935; 1932).

while pregnant or nursing infants and carrying toddlers along with their loads. But gathering is a protracted activity, of more continuous but less intense character overall than hunting, which typically involves short periods of sustained high energy expenditure separated by periods of relative inactivity. Whether tracking large game on African savannas or birds and monkeys in Amazonian rain forests, hunters typically have to walk and run quietly for miles, leaving base camp for days and weeks on end. It is not difficult, therefore, to see why both sexes would consider it more reasonable for the men to travel the long distances to track fast-moving game, often over such long periods, free of cumbersome (and noisy!) dependent nursing infants and toddlers.

But why would this natural division of labor which would benefit both sexes in itself be the source of incipient inequalities? The answer to that question seems to lie in the fact that while hunting seems to have developed as a secondary activity relative to gathering, the meat provided by the hunters is valued much more highly by the entire society than gathered foods:

> In light of the greater importance of gathered food in the diet, it is curious that all !Kung, both men and women, value meat more highly than plant food. When meat is scarce in the camp, all people express a craving for it, even when vegetable foods are abundant. And the occasions when large animals are killed are usually marked by feasting, dancing and the giving of gifts of meat. As game animals are scarce and unpredictable compared with plant foods, it is perhaps not so surprising that hunting is invested with more symbolic significance than gathering; and one should not lose sight of the fact that hunting provides essential nutrients, such as high quality protein, which are not as readily available from plant foods alone. (Lee 1979, p. 451)

Shostak describes a typical scene when meat is brought back to a camp:

> Squeals of delighted children may greet women as they return from gathering, but when men walk into the village balancing meat on sticks held high on their shoulders, everyone celebrates, young and old alike. It may even precipitate a trance dance. The one thing women can bring in that causes a comparable reaction is honey, but the finding of honey is a much rarer event and one that men are usually enlisted to help with. !Kung women may control the distribution of their gathered products, but the distribution of meat, while more constrained by formal rules, involves men in a wider sphere of influence. (Shostak 1981, p. 243)

While it is beyond the scope of this essay to attempt comparative reviews of the organization of different gatherer-hunter societies, it can be noted that the same basic pattern can be found, for instance, among the Iticoteri Indians who live deep in the Amazonian rain forests: the women do the bulk of the gathering (and fishing, accomplished by dumping plant toxins in nearby streams and harvesting the fish which then float to the surface) and the men take on the tasks of hunting; game is scarce and many hunts unsuccessful, but any meat is highly valued and the men distribute the meat (Donner 1982).

There is no reason to suggest that the fact that the men might distribute the prized meat would have been the source of social conflicts in the development of the gathering-hunting way of life. In the absence of chieftains, strict hierarchies, or any ruling bodies, the distribution of hunted meat would most likely have proceeded like the distribution of the gathered plant foods: whoever brought it in, parceled it out. But because meat seems to be so highly prized in gatherer-hunter societies, because hunting, unlike gathering, could not be regularly engaged in by both sexes, and because individuals in such societies typically distribute themselves what they bring in, it is easy to understand why men would secure a certain extra measure of social influence in such societies—the first, embryonic basis for the domination of women by men. All this tends to strongly reinforce the view that there has *never* been any genetic basis, any innate predisposition of "human nature," for the domination of women by men and that its origin—and its endpoint—are inextricably linked to the origin and development of various forms of division of labor instituted for the purpose of expanding the material base of various societies. It is neither, therefore, something that is inherent in either sex nor something that is inevitable or immutable.

At some point in our distant past it must have become clear to early humans of both sexes that they could all benefit from a parceling out of tasks which would enable *all* members of the society to expand their material subsistence base. This is most likely to have occurred after the gathering mode of obtaining food had been well established, and a first material surplus generated, in the sense that food supplies beyond what an individual could consume on the spot could be regularly obtained. This then would provide the material basis for that first division of labor and in particular for the freeing up of sections of the society for activities which would be one step further removed from the most direct form of subsistence activity and which would in turn generate the material basis for further expansion of the productive base of society and, increasingly, the further development of activities not directly tied to production such as art, science, religion, etc.

In the early evolution of the hominid line it seems that simple gathering of food may have gone on for at least 2 million years *before* the development of the first crude stone tools appropriate for butchering and later hunting, which occurred about 2 million years ago. The fact that the first known social division of labor (between gathering and hunting activities) most likely fell out along sexual lines due to the necessity of women bearing, nursing, and carrying highly dependent young is nothing to be distressed about. These very same necessities may well have impelled the development of systematic gathering of food surpluses in the first place, making the earliest division of labor possible. And without division of labor, human beings could not have gone beyond the stultifying ways of a literal "hand-to-mouth" existence. The earliest division of labor spurred the further development of the productive base of the society, providing not just more and better food, but an impetus for the further development of tools and methods of production, and the basis from which to explore and transform the external world as never before. And finally it should be said that the biological necessities associated with bearing children are themselves not immutable or necessarily permanent factors, and eventually the further elaboration of human social organization will be such that biological attributes will no longer contribute to channeling or restricting the activities of half the human species.

IV

In the 100 or so years since the first attempt to apply the methodology of dialectical and historical materialism to the investigation of development and change in human societies, a clearer understanding has emerged of the relationship which exists at any given time between the *economic base* of a society (its relations of production—of ownership of the means of production and also the division of labor and relations of distribution—which in turn correspond to a certain level of development of productive forces) and that society's *superstructure* (its political and cultural institutions, prevailing ideas, etc.). One would think by now that all but the most stubborn philistines of hard-core idealists and religious obscurantists would be able to see that human cultural and political institutions do not stand in some idealized vacuum, somehow separated from the realm of human productive activities. And an historical materialist approach demands consistency: current social institutions and social relations cannot be acknowledged to have had their *roots* in the forms of production and divi-

139

sion of labor of society in the distant past and yet be treated as if they no longer had a similar basis in modern times, as if the preservation and reproduction of certain social relations (including those involving subjugation and oppression) was simply a matter of social "attitudes and policies" in the abstract. Conversely, these questions cannot be approached with a mechanical, economic-determinist slant, as if, for instance, every major development in the productive forces of a society immediately and automatically brought about major changes in the social relations and superstructure of the society—an incorrect notion which leads to the view that all that is needed to rid society of backward social relations is to expand production, modernize and unleash state-of-the-art technologies, etc.

A dialectical approach calls for grasping the contradictory motion inherent in all processes in nature and society. There is no doubt that the economic base of a society is fundamentally determined by the level of development of the productive forces of that society—whether a given group of people have a few simple gathering and hunting implements, or domesticated herds and agricultural plots, or large-scale industrial production will set the stage for the types of production relations which will characterize that society and render it recognizable in the main as a gatherer-hunter, herding, agricultural (slave or feudal), or advanced industrial society. But this nexus of social production relations will at any given point spawn particular superstructural forms which serve to preserve and perpetuate these social production relations.

That these social production relations are the basic determinants of the overall character of a society should be obvious from the simple fact that it is not possible to graft any old superstructure onto a given economic base—imagine attempting to graft the governing structures, cultural institutions, and dominant ideologies of an industrial capitalist society onto the economic base of a foraging society or vice versa: it simply couldn't be done without rupturing the whole fabric of society. But while the productive base of a society spawns a particular superstructure and imposes certain limits and restrictions or developmental constraints upon this superstructure at any given time, these two spheres exist in a state of dialectical interaction. As the continually developing productive forces of society come into conflict with the existing production relations, the necessary revolution in this economic base is restrained, prevented by the very superstructural forms which it spawned to facilitate its own reproduction but which now can only serve to hold society in the grip of the outmoded relations. This is why, time and time again, human beings have to reach up and forcibly shatter the dead weight of this superstructural lid in order to breathe new life into every aspect of social organization and fundamentally to transform the relations of production —these are the recurring social revolutions which punctuate human history, those tremendous qualitative leaps and ruptures in the social order through which society casts off its strangling sheath and reemerges on an often initially vulnerable, but dramatically restructured basis.

At any one point, previous social history imposes certain developmental constraints—the road ahead does not present an infinite variety of options for change; yet there is also never a single, straight-line, narrow path which necessarily predetermines the direction of change. And it is, in fact, important to break with a philosophical misconception present in early Marxist thought, known as the negation of the negation, which holds, as a basic law of dialectics, that development proceeds through the overcoming (negation) of a given thing, and then its reemergence (or the reemergence of major aspects of it) on a higher level through the next negation. This is a view which has been challenged by

Mao Tsetung, and most recently by Bob Avakian (cf. especially Avakian 1979, pp. 182-85). In an example given by Engels of the negation of the negation, a barley seed is said to be negated by the plant which it gives rise to, which is in turn negated by the seed(s) which it produces. But what if the initial grain is ground down? What if the plant produces multiple seeds, some of which germinate, while others rot, etc.? Such possible alternate routes cannot be so easily dismissed as peripheral diversions to a basic law of development as Engels seemed to think.

This point has crucial implications for views of social change, because it suggests that if, for instance, the subjugation of women today is inextricably intertwined with the existence of exploitative class relations, then this automatically must mean that the stage of society which the emergence of classes "negated," i.e. primitive communal society, must have been completely free of any inequities between the sexes (which is very unlikely, given that there was from the beginning a division of labor between the sexes and therefore differential participation in certain activities, even if these differences could in no way be construed to constitute oppression). Similarly, a future classless society (communism) should not be viewed as a negation of class societies and a resurrection of primitive communalism (albeit on a higher level), an incorrect view which is evident in Engels as he ends *The Origin of the Family, Private Property, and the State* with a quote from Morgan, who aspires to a future society where property will cease to govern all and be the "end and aim" and where there will be "a revival, in a higher form, of the liberty, equality and fraternity of the ancient gentes" (p. 237). Not only does this notion of the negation of the negation tend toward an idealist (and metaphysical) view of primitive communal society, it also tends to promote such a view towards social development overall and toward the communist society of the future. As Bob Avakian has pointed out:

> Specifically in regard to the development of society, the concept of negation of the negation will tend to present a "closed system" of development leading to communism and promote a static, "absolutist" view of communism itself as the end product of the negation of the negation and the kingdom of "great harmony." As opposed to this, Mao declares in his 1964 talk on philosophy: "Communism will last for thousands and thousands of years, I don't believe that there will be no qualitative changes under communism, that it will not be divided into stages by qualitative changes! I don't believe it!... This is unthinkable in the light of dialectics." (1979, p. 185)

Communist society will mean the abolition of class distinctions and social inequalities—including that between men and women and the oppression of the latter by the former—but it will do this on the foundation of human cultural development (in the broadest sense) up to this point, and by making a great leap from and beyond this, and not by resurrecting, even on a "higher level," an idealized primitive communal society which in reality contained the seeds, if only the seeds, of these very class distinctions and social inequalities and which was bound to give rise to forms of society in which they would be fundamental.

The oppression of women does not have its origin in the fact that the female of the species bears the young, and even the first social division of labor with the emergence of a gathering and hunting way of life could only carry within it the seeds of this oppression, a mere suggestion of it. Oppression and exploitation among human beings in fact does not seem to result from the division of labor where conditions are such that the basis for a growing accumulation of surplus remains very limited and therefore not in sharp contradiction with prevailing "egalitarian" communal modes of organization. But wherever and whenever a social division of labor has occurred in conditions such that it made possible a significant accumulation of surplus beyond what would be used up almost immediately by the society as a whole, then the basis existed for individuals or sections of people to monopolize the means of production and the superstructure of politics, science, art, religion, and so on, and on that basis rule over other human beings. For a long time there had not been the possibility to break out of this basic pattern because humanity had not yet developed a sufficient material basis to be able to maintain existing productive forces (including all the people) and develop them *further still*, without some kind of division of labor that involved exploitation and oppression.

As already discussed, in the earliest divisions of labor, women may well have been the economic mainstays of society, providing the bulk of the food consumed through gathering. But it is the hunting activities of the men and the provision of meat which would more likely have conferred a basis for special social status and control, and the sporadic character of most hunting (intense periods of activity followed by often prolonged periods of inactivity as opposed to the more ongoing character of gathering) may have provided the men with greater opportunities to engage in nonproductive activities such as art, religious ritual, etc.

Less tied down by the young, the men would also range farther afield than the women and therefore have greater occasion to explore new areas and encounter other groups. Men therefore would likely have been the most common initiators of exchanges between groups; whether these exchanges would be friendly or not would depend on any number of circumstances. Any given encounter, of course, need not have been antagonistic, and friendly coexistence and cooperation must indeed have been commonplace. But there must have been many situations where, given the generally quite limited productive capacities and, on the other hand, the newfound abilities to store and accumulate surpluses, discrepancies in material accumulation would have taken on more significance. Such *unevenness*, rather than some precise degree of accumulation, is likely to have been the most important factor spurring the early development of large-scale social divisions in human societies. While, again, no given encounter need have been antagonistic, the point is that *now*, when antagonisms did flare up for whatever reasons (personal disagreements, or, increasingly, conflicts rooted in uneven material accumulation or different concepts of "ownership") there *would* be something to plunder (and to defend!), and the material basis would exist for people's actions to exacerbate even further the differences in material reserves between them—to the benefit of some and to the detriment of others.

Men, who in the course of hunting typically ranged further than women and used weapons more routinely, would also more likely be in a position to carry out raids on the reserves of other groups—appropriating food and implements or even human beings they were able to capture, who at first would most likely be the less mobile women and the young. These might often have been simply incorporated into their captors' groups, not necessarily with much coercion, and would join in the productive activities of the society, in a sense becoming part of its "reserves." Just as men controlled the differential reproduction of the much-coveted meat in foraging societies (through which they acquired a certain measure of differential status and control), in societies where plunder emerged as a consistent social activity they would likely regulate the distribution of women and young who, by contributing to the productive activities of their new group, might acquire a kind of exchange value, be traded, given as gifts, etc. The point is not that this would happen overnight (nor certainly that it was somehow biologically predetermined!) but that, as the material base of society expanded further on a foundation of unevenness (the social unevenness within a group stemming from the division of labor and the unevenness between different groups with different material bases), women would quite likely be encompassed in the developing concept of property. As such they would increasingly be subject to rules and regulations designed to strictly control their sexual activities and production of young—hence the origin of rules barring them from having more than one mate, whereas in many cases men would continue to have more than one "wife."[33] As the productive base of the society developed, it is not difficult to see how such a system could have been expanded to include the taking of male slaves, especially once the productive activities had expanded to include early organized plantings which would provide much greater food reserves, the need for more stationary lifestyles, the capacity to sustain much larger groups, and a shift to a form of production (agri-

---

[33]The degree of polygyny of the men would be likely to correlate closely with the material reserves they controlled or could depend on. In the !Kung, for instance, most of the men have only one official wife; although a second is accepted and even a source of status, most !Kung men simply cannot provide enough meat to "afford" a second wife and extended family, including obligations to more relatives, etc. !Kung women are typically married a number of times during their lives, but while they may have a number of unofficial lovers, they do not have more than one official "husband" at one time. And !Kung women often oppose (and may succeed in preventing) their husband's taking a second wife, even though this co-wife could help her in gathering and other activities. Such resistance to a co-wife often seems at least partly related to the fact that the man's additional obligations might reduce the amount of meat available for the first wife and her children.

culture) requiring the intense labor of a number of people in a delimited area.

One area which needs much further investigation is that of the development and implications of the division of labor between men and women in *transitions* from foraging societies to horticultural societies. Engels makes the assumption, which was widely held until recent years, that men were typically responsible for providing the bulk of food resources in primitive societies; he did not realize the extent to which women actually tend to supply the bulk of the food consumed in foraging societies through their gathering activities. The control of production and distribution of food as the economic base expanded to include animal husbandry and the earliest forms of agriculture were therefore assumed by Engels to have generally been in the hands of men, as a natural outgrowth of their prior activities. Engels also thought that the domestication of herds preceded the domestication of plants—in fact, both practices may well have arisen simultaneously or in reverse order, depending on geographical locality, seasonal changes, etc. If men typically engaged in most of the hunting, it is quite possible that they initiated the domestication of animals and controlled the first herds. Conversely women's gathering activities would likely have taught them to be very observant of plant ways (in primitive societies women usually know more about medicinal herbs, for instance, even where spiritual healing and the use of hallucinogenic plants is often the restricted province of men); observing the germination of seeds and the sprouting of tubers which they gathered, women may well have initiated the first plantings and tended the first garden plots (women do in fact tend the gardens and fields in basic horticultural systems) and stored grain. It is not clear how the distribution of crops was typically handled nor how men entered this sphere of activity as the importance of hunting declined. Perhaps men initiated the acquisition and control of slaves ("the human cattle") to expand the agricultural activities, thereby displacing the women in this sphere and gaining control over the fields and distribution of crops.

In speaking of the emergence of classes, Engels explained that:

> The cleavage of society into an exploiting and an exploited class, a ruling and an oppressed class, was the necessary outcome of the previous low development of production. Society is necessarily divided into classes as long as the total social labour only yields a product but slightly exceeding what is necessary for the bare existence of all, as long as labour therefore claims all or almost all the time of the great majority of the members of society. Side by side with this great majority exclusively enthralled in toil, a class freed from direct productive labour is formed which manages the general business of society: the direction of labour, affairs of state, justice, science, art, and so forth. It is therefore the law of the division of labour which lies at the root of the division into classes. (Engels 1878, p. 369)

It is simply an indication of the remaining primitiveness of human societies that the further expansion and transformation of the material bases of societies up to this point could not occur without such societal divisions and the resulting exploitation and oppression of large sections of humanity. But we have now reached the stage where the material basis exists to go beyond this type of social organization and in fact these social divisions, far from furthering the development of the material base of human society, are actually, *and for the first time in history, preventing* this further development. As Engels put it:

> In fact the abolition of social classes presupposes a level of historical development at which the exis-

tence not merely of this or that particular ruling class but of any ruling class at all, and therefore of class distinction itself, has become an anachronism, is obsolete. It therefore presupposes that the development of production has reached a level at which the appropriation of the means of production and of the products, and consequently of political supremacy and of the monopoly of education and intellectual leadership by a special social class, has become not only superfluous but also a hindrance to development economically, politically and intellectually. (Engels 1878, pp. 364-65)

Today, in the age of imperialism, the dominant relations of production in the world are those of a highly integrated and interconnected worldwide system. It is a period characterized by a tremendously acute contradiction between private ownership and appropriation of the means of production, and socialized use of these means. To a greater extent than ever before, the world's productive forces must be used in common, as atomized, small-scale individual production is fast being replaced by large-scale production activities requiring the coordinated participation of great numbers of people. The existing lopsidedness[34] in the world makes it all the more unlikely that the needed fundamental restructuring of social relations will be achieved on a world scale in

---

[34]I have taken this term from Bob Avakian, who writes, for example: "This era of imperialism and the proletarian revolution and the problem of the transition to communism worldwide have been further complicated by what I described in *Conquer the World* as the 'lopsidedness in the world.' What this refers to is the fact that in the world today the advanced productive forces are concentrated in a handful of the advanced—that is, imperialist—countries while the economies of most of the countries in the world are not simply backward but distorted, disarticulated in their development because of imperialist domination and plunder" (Avakian 1983, p. 144).

one fell swoop, but the basis does exist for this global transformation and there are immediate prospects for taking some major steps in that direction, by overthrowing and dismantling whenever and wherever possible the superstructural dead weights, the lids which are serving to maintain the existing division of labor in place, with all the unnecessary misery and oppression that it entails for the great majority of humanity.

How ironic and revealing, then, that just as we finally attain a level where a material basis exists for doing away with oppression and exploitation on a global scale, there are long lines of apologists in the sciences and the media who are bending over backwards to find some kind—any kind—of proof for the notion that there are some unchanging innate characteristics of human nature which would make this leap impossible: the more historical material evidence surfaces to contradict their arguments, the more frantically they seem to seek such proofs, forced to look further and further back in time to our earliest origins, and yet still unable to provide a single shred of evidence for the supposed innateness and unchangeability of human social characteristics. What an outlook—and what a system reflected and served by it—that wants and needs to search desperately, against ever-accumulating evidence to the contrary, for some "innate" reason why the exploitation and oppression of one part of humanity by another cannot be overcome! And yet all of human history and our very biology combine to point in the opposite direction, revealing what is in fact our tremendous behavioral plasticity and capacity for social change in relation to changes in external material conditions, which we are increasingly able to effect and shape.

The solution to the problems of social divisions and inequities in the modern world—including that of the domination and oppression of women—continues to be masked by innumerable unsubstantiated "origin myths" based on biological or cultural determinism. They are all fundamentally idealist, both because they base themselves on assumptions for which there is no evidence and which are rendered unlikely by actual material developments (such as the notion of a specific genetic basis for specific social behaviors in humans) *and* because they fail to recognize and to take into account existing material social conditions which set the terms for change in human societies (such as the incipient basis for the oppression of women in the earliest social division of labor along sex lines). The basis for the elimination of exploitation and oppression among human beings is now in sight, although this leap will require a total upheaval of prevailing economic and political relations and a thoroughgoing revolutionization in the realm of ideas. This leap would be as significant and defining to all future human life as that represented by the first emergence of the capacity to gather a surplus of food was to all human history up to this point. This time also, the female of the species would play a crucial, in fact essential, role in effecting the leap, but with the result this time being her complete emancipation along with that of humanity as a whole from all forms of oppression and social inequality.

Appendix:
Why was Engels
one step ahead?

In relation to the persistence of idealist "origin myths," it is useful to reflect on the tenacity of the particular myth of "brain primacy." This idea remained deeply entrenched in prevailing theories of human evolution at least until the 1920s when remains of early *Australopithecines* were discovered, revealing that they had small brains but erect posture.[35] The essential feature of this myth resides in the notion that what distinguishes *Homo sapiens* from the rest of the animal world is the realm of ideas: thought, as separate from any material, physical capacities and interactions with other matter. In many religious myths and other idealist systems of thought this took the form of idealized dichotomies between "body" and "soul" or between "mat-

---

[35]For an entertaining and thought-provoking discussion of how the tenacity of the brain-primacy myth contributed to the long acceptance of the Piltdown Man fraud, and how it continues to be resurrected in modern literature such as Arthur Koestler's work, see Gould 1980, pp. 108-124, 131.

ter" and "reason." In modern times, and especially since Darwin's theories of natural and sexual selection highlighted the material bases for the emergence and transformation of all life-forms and their underlying interconnectedness, it became much more difficult to attempt to isolate humans from such processes and attribute to them qualities of demigods. Many therefore beat a partial retreat, recognizing that humans were also a product of material processes of natural selection but clinging to the notion that the key step mediating the evolutionary divergence away from the ancestral apes had been the emergence of that locus of all well-reasoned thought and well-ordered policy, the human brain.

It is now, however, unquestionably clear from the fossil record that the expansion of the brain was *not* the key feature in the divergence of the hominid line from the apes; instead, the initiating and decisive step was the emergence of bipedality and the attendant freeing of the hands for activities other than locomotion. Thus there is no doubt that our divergence away from the ancestral apes was not mediated by any special reasoning abilities as distinct from our capacity to transform matter, but the other way around: key changes in our capacity to transform matter, through labor, laid the basis for the development of our brains and capacities for abstract reasoning.

There has historically been so much resistance to this notion that the myth of brain primacy remained the prevailing view even among evolutionary scientists until just a few decades ago, when the fossil record made it clear that bipedality came first. But this was not simply a question of ignorance which could only be dispelled by the discovery of more material evidence in the form of fossils. Long before fossils had been discovered which would provide this "proof," a handful of scientists (notably Ernst Haeckel) had questioned the theory of brain primacy and suggested that bipedality was the feature which had played the key role in the divergence from the apes. This "minority view" was shared by Engels, who in 1876 wrote *On the Part Played by Labour in the Transition From Ape to Man,* an essay which was largely ignored but which forcefully put forward the view that the transition from the apes must initially have been mediated by the evolution of erect posture which would have freed the hands for labor. This Engels termed *"the decisive step in the transition from ape to man."*

Labor, Engels stressed, is not simply the source of all wealth in human societies, but "the primary basic condition for all human existence" (1876, p. 279). In reflecting on the tremendous resistance to this theory in the scientific circles of his day, Engels wrote that with the development of human societies there emerged not only the more developed forms of production of agriculture and industry, but also art, science, complex social organization, laws, and religion:

> In the face of all these creations, which appeared in the first place to be products of the mind, and which seemed to dominate human society, the more modest productions of the working hand retreated into the background, the more so since the mind that plans the labour process already at a very early stage of development of society (*e.g.* already in the simpl[e] family), was able to have the labour that had been planned carried out by other hands than its own. All merit for the swift advance of civilisation was ascribed to the mind, to the development and activity of the brain. Men became accustomed to explain their actions from their thoughts, instead of from their needs—(which in any case are reflected and come to consciousness in the mind) — and so there arose in the course of time that idealistic outlook on the world which, especially since the decline of the ancient world, has dominated men's

minds. It still rules them to such a degree that even the most materialistic natural scientists of the Darwinian school are still unable to form any clear idea of the origin of man, because under this ideological influence they do not recognize the part that has been played therein by labour. (Engels 1876, p. 289)

How could Engels be so much closer to the truth than the majority of the "scientific experts" of his time? The reason lay in his application of the dialectical and historical materialist method, which had made it possible for Marx and Engels to understand the basic defining features and bases for change in different human societies over time. They were able to understand that any given human society is characterized by the prevailing modes of production corresponding to certain productive forces and by the relations between human beings relative to these processes of production, and they grasped that this has been the essential base from which flowed particular political and ideological institutions and ideas, rather than the other way around. They were also able to analyze the major historical discontinuities, the major social upheavals which mediated the transitions from one type of society to another (e.g. the transition from feudalism to capitalism). These, they said, had their origins in the fact that society's productive forces had developed to a point where they were increasingly stifled and restricted by the production relations and superstructural forms which they had originally spawned. This intensifying contradiction could only be resolved through the breakup and overthrow of this societal dead weight. This understanding of the dialectical process of social change, rooted in historically conditioned material developments in production, made it possible to tie together and encompass all previous human history in all its diversity and complexity and to distill from this the basic laws of social change. This is no doubt what enabled Engels to see with such insight into the factors which mediated the transition from ape to human. If these insights were largely ignored for decades, today they are no longer deniable, even by those who, while grudgingly recognizing the incontestable evidence, continue to mutter lamely about the invalidity of Marxism.

References

Avakian, Bob. 1979. *Mao Tsetung's Immortal Contributions.* Chicago: RCP Publications.

—————. 1983. *For a Harvest of Dragons: On the "Crisis of Marxism" and the Power of Marxism, Now More Than Ever.* Chicago: RCP Publications.

Chorover, Stephan L. 1980. *From Genesis to Genocide: The Meaning of Human Nature and the Power of Behavior Control.* Cambridge: MIT Press.

Donner, Florinda. 1982. *Shabono.* New York: Delacorte Press.

Eldredge, Niles, and Stephen Jay Gould. 1972. Punctuated equilibria: an alternative to phyletic gradualism. In *Models in Paleobiology,* edited by T.M. Schopf. San Francisco: Freeman, Cooper & Co.

Engels, Frederick. 1876. On the part played by labour in the transition from ape to man. In *Dialectics of Nature,* by Engels. New York: International Publishers, 1940 ed.

—————. 1878. *Anti-Dühring.* Peking: Foreign Languages Press, 1976 ed.

—————. 1884. *The Origin of the Family, Private Property, and the State,* with an introduction by Eleanor Burke Leacock. New York: International Publishers, 1940 ed.

Flannery, Regina. 1932. The position of women among the Mescalero Apache. *Primitive Man* 10:26-32.

—————. 1935. The position of women among the Eastern Cree. *Primitive Man* 12: 81-86.

Frisch, Rose E. 1978. Population, food intake and fertility. *Science* 199:22-30.

Gould, Stephen Jay. 1977. *Ever Since Darwin.* New York: W. W. Norton.

—————. 1978. Sociobiology: the art of storytelling. *New Scientist* 80:530-533.

—————. 1980. *The Panda's Thumb.* New York: W.W. Norton.

—————. 1981. *The Mismeasure of Man.* New York: W.W. Norton.

—————. 1983. *Hen's Teeth and Horse's Toes.* New York: W. W. Norton.

Gould, Stephen Jay, and Niles Eldredge. 1977. Punctuated equilibria: the tempo and mode of evolution reconsidered. *Paleobiology* 3:115-151.

Gould, Stephen Jay, and R. C. Lewontin. 1979. The spandrels of San Marco and the Panglossian paradigm: a critique of the adaptationist programme. *Proceedings of the Royal Society of London* B205:581-598.

Gould, Stephen Jay, and Elisabeth S. Vrba. 1982. Exaptation—a missing term in the science of form. *Paleobiology* 8(1):4-15.

Hrdy, Sarah Blaffer. 1981. *The Woman That Never Evolved.* Cambridge: Harvard University Press.

Kurtén, Björn. 1978. *Dance of the Tiger: A Novel of the Ice Age,* with an introduction by Stephen Jay Gould. New York: Berkley Books.

Lee, Richard B. 1979. *The !Kung San: Men, Women and Work in a Foraging Society.* New York: Cambridge University Press.

Lewontin, Richard C. 1979. Sociobiology as an adaptationist program. *Behavioral Science* 24:5-14.

Lewontin, R. C., Steven Rose, and Leon J. Kamin. 1984. *Not in Our Genes: Biology, Ideology, and Human Nature.* New York: Pantheon Books.

Lorenz, Konrad. 1966. *On Aggression.* New York: Harcourt Brace Jovanovich.

Marx, Karl. 1859. *Preface and Introduction to a Contribution to the Critique of Political Economy.* Peking: Foreign Languages Press, 1976 ed.

Mayr, Ernst. 1982. *The Growth of Biological Thought—Diversity, Evolution and Inheritance.* Cambridge: Harvard University Press.

————. 1983. How to carry out the adaptationist program? *American Naturalist* 121:324-334.

Morgan, Elaine. 1971. *The Descent of Woman.* New York: Stein and Day.

Savage-Rumbaugh, E. Sue, and Beverly J. Wilkerson. 1978. Sociosexual behavior in *Pan paniscus* and *Pan troglodytes:* a comparative study. *Journal of Human Evolution* 7:327-344.

Shostak, Marjorie. 1981. *Nisa: The Life and Words of a !Kung Woman.* Cambridge: Harvard University Press.

Tanner, Nancy Makepeace. 1981. *On Becoming Human.* New York: Cambridge University Press.

Wilson, Edward O. 1978. *On Human Nature.* Cambridge: Harvard University Press.